OFFICIAL SQA PAST PAPERS WITH ANSWERS

INTERMEDIATE 2

CHEMISTRY
2006-2009

First exam published in 2006.
Published by Bright Red Publishing Ltd, 6 Stafford Street, Edinburgh EH3 7AU
tel: 0131 220 5804 fax: 0131 220 6710 info@brightredpublishing.co.uk www.brightredpublishing.co.uk

ISBN 978-1-84948-039-0

A CIP Catalogue record for this book is available from the British Library.

Bright Red Publishing is grateful to the copyright holders, as credited on the final page of the book, for permission to use their material.
Every effort has been made to trace the copyright holders and to obtain their permission for the use of copyright material.
Bright Red Publishing will be happy to receive information allowing us to rectify any error or omission in future editions.

[BLANK PAGE]

FOR OFFICIAL USE

Section B   **Total Marks**   [ ]

X012/201

NATIONAL
QUALIFICATIONS
2006

TUESDAY, 30 MAY
9.00 AM – 11.00 AM

CHEMISTRY
INTERMEDIATE 2

Fill in these boxes and read what is printed below.

Full name of centre

[   ]

Town

[   ]

Forename(s)

[   ]

Surname

[   ]

Date of birth
Day Month Year

[ ][ ][ ][ ][ ][ ]

Scottish candidate number

[ ][ ][ ][ ][ ][ ][ ][ ]

Number of seat

[   ]

Necessary data will be found in the Chemistry Data Booklet for Standard Grade and Intermediate 2 (1999 Edition).

Section A – Questions 1–30 (30 marks)

Instructions for completion of **Section A** are given on page two.

For this section of the examination you must use an **HB pencil**.

Section B (50 marks)

All questions should be attempted.

The questions may be answered in any order but all answers are to be written in the spaces provided in this answer book, **and must be written clearly and legibly in ink**.

Rough work, if any should be necessary, should be written in this book, and then scored through when the fair copy has been written. If further space is required, a supplementary sheet for rough work may be obtained from the invigilator.

Additional space for answers will be found at the end of the book. If further space is required, supplementary sheets may be obtained from the invigilator and should be inserted inside the **front** cover of this booklet.

Before leaving the examination room you must give this book to the invigilator. If you do not, you may lose all the marks for this paper.

SCOTTISH
QUALIFICATIONS
AUTHORITY

Read carefully

1   Check that the answer sheet provided is for **Chemistry Intermediate 2 (Section A)**.

2   For this section of the examination you must use an **HB pencil** and, where necessary, an eraser.

3   Check that the answer sheet you have been given has **your name**, **date of birth**, **SCN** (Scottish Candidate Number) and **Centre Name** printed on it.

    Do not change any of these details.

4   If any of this information is wrong, tell the Invigilator immediately.

5   If this information is correct, **print** your name and seat number in the boxes provided.

6   The answer to each question is **either** A, B, C or D. Decide what your answer is, then, using your pencil, put a horizontal line in the space provided (see sample question below).

7   There is **only one correct** answer to each question.

8   Any rough working should be done on the question paper or the rough working sheet, **not** on your answer sheet.

9   At the end of the exam, put the **answer sheet for Section A inside the front cover of this answer book**.

Sample Question

To show that the ink in a ball-pen consists of a mixture of dyes, the method of separation would be

         A   chromatography

         B   fractional distillation

         C   fractional crystallisation

         D   filtration.

The correct answer is **A**—chromatography. The answer **A** has been clearly marked in **pencil** with a horizontal line (see below).

Changing an answer

If you decide to change your answer, carefully erase your first answer and using your pencil, fill in the answer you want. The answer below has been changed to **D**.

SECTION A

1. Which of the following elements is an alkali metal?

   A Aluminium

   B Calcium

   C Copper

   D Sodium

2. Lemonade can be made by dissolving sugar, lemon juice and carbon dioxide in water. In lemonade, the solvent is

   A water

   B sugar

   C lemon juice

   D carbon dioxide.

3. The mass number of the atom $^{23}_{11}Na$ is

   A 11

   B 12

   C 23

   D 34.

4. Which of the following is the electron arrangement for a halogen atom?

   (You may wish to use page 1 of the data booklet to help you.)

   A 2, 5

   B 2, 6

   C 2, 7

   D 2, 8

5. The table shows information about some atoms.

Atom	Atomic number	Mass number
W	16	34
X	18	36
Y	18	40
Z	20	40

   Which two atoms are isotopes of the same element?

   A W and X

   B X and Y

   C W and Y

   D Y and Z

6. Which of the following pairs of elements combine to form an ionic compound?

   A Lead and fluorine

   B Sulphur and oxygen

   C Carbon and nitrogen

   D Phosphorus and chlorine

7. Which of the following particles contains a different number of electrons from the others?

   (You may wish to use page 1 of the data booklet to help you.)

   A Cl^-

   B S^{2-}

   C Ar

   D Na^+

8. What is the correct formula for aluminium sulphate?

   A $AlSO_4$

   B $Al(SO_4)_3$

   C $Al_2(SO_4)_3$

   D $Al_3(SO_4)_2$

[Turn over

9. Glucose has the molecular formula $C_6H_{12}O_6$.

   How many moles are contained in 18g of glucose?

   A   0·01

   B   0·1

   C   1

   D   10

10. 0·2 mol of gas has a mass of 12·8 g.

    Which of the following could be the molecular formula for the gas?

    A SO_2

    B CO

    C CO_2

    D NH_3

11. Catalytic converters speed up the conversion of harmful gases to less harmful gases. Which of the following reactions is most likely to occur in a catalytic converter?

    A   Carbon dioxide reacting to form carbon monoxide

    B   Carbon monoxide reacting to form carbon dioxide

    C   Nitrogen reacting to form nitrogen dioxide

    D   Oxygen reacting to form hydrogen oxide

12. Heavy gas oil produced by the fractional distillation of crude oil has a high viscosity.

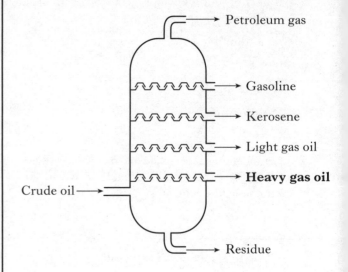

   Which of the following properties also apply to heavy gas oil?

   A   Low boiling point and high flammability

   B   High boiling point and high flammability

   C   Low boiling point and low flammability

   D   High boiling point and low flammability

13.

   (structural formulae diagrams)

   The above structural formulae represent

   A   the same hydrocarbon

   B   different hydrocarbons

   C   isomers

   D   isotopes.

14. The first three members of the alkanone series are:

$$
\begin{array}{c}
\quad\;\; H \quad O \quad H \\
\quad\;\; | \quad\; \| \quad\; | \\
H - C - C - C - H \\
\quad\;\; | \qquad\; | \\
\quad\;\; H \qquad\; H
\end{array}
\qquad
\begin{array}{c}
\quad\;\; H \quad O \quad H \quad H \\
\quad\;\; | \quad\; \| \quad\; | \quad\; | \\
H - C - C - C - C - H \\
\quad\;\; | \qquad\; | \quad\; | \\
\quad\;\; H \qquad\; H \quad H
\end{array}
\qquad
\begin{array}{c}
\quad\;\; H \quad O \quad H \quad H \quad H \\
\quad\;\; | \quad\; \| \quad\; | \quad\; | \quad\; | \\
H - C - C - C - C - C - H \\
\quad\;\; | \qquad\; | \quad\; | \quad\; | \\
\quad\;\; H \qquad\; H \quad H \quad H
\end{array}
$$

What is the general formula for this homologous series?

A $C_nH_{2n-2}O$

B $C_nH_{2n}O$

C $C_nH_{2n+1}O$

D $C_nH_{2n+2}O$

15. Which of the following is a structural formula for propyl ethanoate?

A
$$
\begin{array}{c}
\qquad\quad O \\
\qquad\quad \| \\
CH_3 - C - O - CH_2 - CH_3
\end{array}
$$

B
$$
\begin{array}{c}
\qquad\quad O \\
\qquad\quad \| \\
CH_3 - C - O - CH_2 - CH_2 - CH_3
\end{array}
$$

C
$$
\begin{array}{c}
\qquad\qquad\qquad O \\
\qquad\qquad\qquad \| \\
CH_3 - CH_2 - C - O - CH_2 - CH_3
\end{array}
$$

D
$$
\begin{array}{c}
\qquad\qquad\qquad O \\
\qquad\qquad\qquad \| \\
CH_3 - CH_2 - C - O - CH_2 - CH_2 - CH_3
\end{array}
$$

16. The structural formula for hydrocarbon **X** is

$$
\begin{array}{c}
H \qquad\;\; H \quad H \\
| \qquad\;\; | \quad\; | \\
C = C - C - C - H \\
| \quad\; | \quad\; | \quad\; | \\
H \quad H \quad H \quad H
\end{array}
$$

Which of the following statements about hydrocarbon **X** is true?

A   **X** is named but-2-ene.

B   **X** is a saturated hydrocarbon.

C   **X** rapidly decolourises bromine solution.

D   **X** belongs to the group of hydrocarbons with general formula C_nH_{2n+2}.

17. A hydrocarbon was cracked.

The equation for one reaction taking place is shown.

$$C_{22}H_{46} \rightarrow C_{18}H_{38} + \mathbf{Y}$$

What is the molecular formula for **Y**?

A C_3H_8

B C_4H_8

C C_4H_{10}

D C_5H_{12}

18. The method used to increase the ethanol concentration of fermentation products is

A   cracking

B   dehydration

C   distillation

D   hydrolysis.

[Turn over

19. The structure below shows a section of an addition polymer.

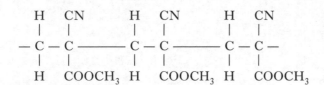

Which molecule is used to make this polymer?

A
```
    H    CN
    |    |
    C =  C
    |    |
    H   COOCH₃
```

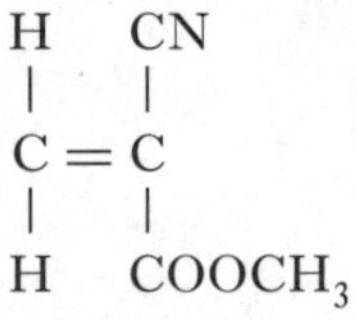

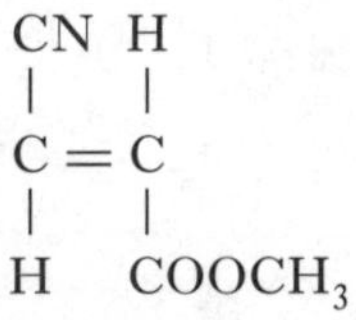

B
```
   CN   H
    |    |
    C =  C
    |    |
    H   COOCH₃
```

C
```
   CN  COOCH₃
    |    |
    C =  C
    |    |
    H    H
```

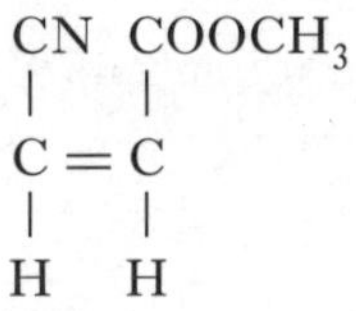

D
```
        H    CN
        |    |
   H  — C  — C — H
        |    |
        H   COOCH₃
```

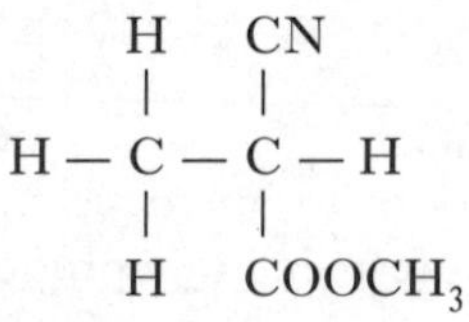

20. To which class of compounds does the hormone insulin belong?

A   Carbohydrates

B   Fats

C   Proteins

D   Hydrocarbons

21.

amino acids $\xrightarrow{\text{reaction } \mathbf{X}}$ protein + water

Which of the following terms describes reaction **X**?

A   Hydration

B   Hydrolysis

C   Dehydration

D   Condensation

22. Which compound could be obtained by the hydrolysis of a fat?

A   Ethanol

B   Glucose

C   Glycerol

D   Propanol

23. When hydrochloric acid with a pH of 3 is diluted with water to give a solution with a pH of 6, the concentration of

A $H^+(aq)$ ions decreases

B $OH^-(aq)$ ions decreases

C $H^+(aq)$ ions and the concentration of $OH^-(aq)$ ions become equal

D $H^+(aq)$ ions and the concentration of $OH^-(aq)$ ions remain unchanged.

24. Which of the following sodium compounds is a base?

A   Sodium carbonate

B   Sodium chloride

C   Sodium nitrate

D   Sodium sulphate

25. When nickel(II) chloride solution is added to sodium carbonate solution an insoluble solid is formed.

A sample of the solid can be separated from the mixture by

A   condensation

B   distillation

C   evaporation

D   filtration.

26. Four cells were made by joining copper, iron, tin and zinc to silver.

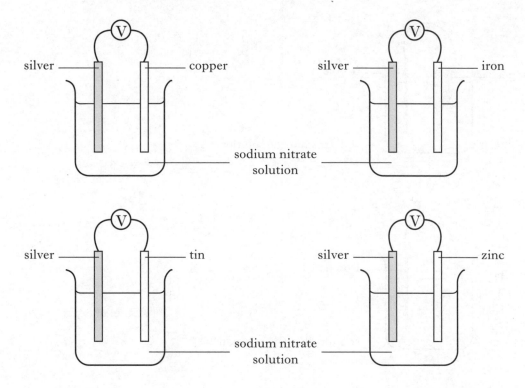

Which of the following will be the voltage of the cell containing silver joined to copper?

(You may wish to use page 7 of the data booklet to help you.)

A   0·5 V

B   0·9 V

C   1·2 V

D   1·6 V

27. A copper(II) chloride solution was electrolysed.

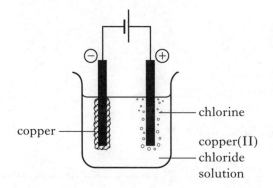

Which of the following changes occurred at the negative electrode?

A   Copper atoms were reduced.

B   Copper atoms were oxidised.

C   Copper ions were reduced.

D   Copper ions were oxidised.

28. Which metal can be extracted from its oxide by heat alone?

A   Lead

B   Mercury

C   Tin

D   Zinc

29. An oil rig can be protected from corrosion by attaching pieces of magnesium to the structure. This method of protection is called

A   galvanising

B   electroplating

C   physical protection

D   sacrificial protection.

[Turn over

30. In which of the following experiments would the iron nail **not** rust?

A

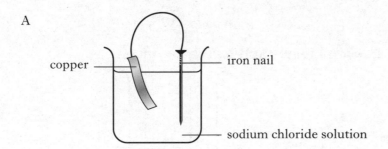

B

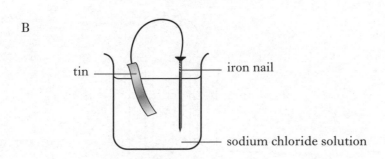

C

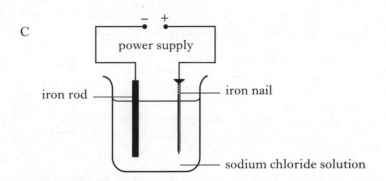

D

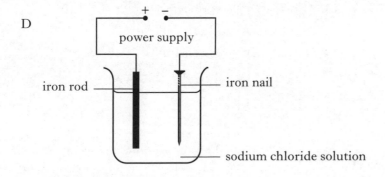

Candidates are reminded that the answer sheet for Section A MUST be placed INSIDE the front cover of this answer book.

DO NOT
WRITE IN
THIS
MARGIN

Marks

SECTION B

50 marks are available in this section of the paper.

All answers must be written clearly and legibly in ink.

1.　Natural gas contains unwanted sulphur compounds.

　　(*a*)　Burning sulphur compounds releases sulphur dioxide into the atmosphere.　What problems can be caused by releasing sulphur dioxide into the atmosphere?

　　　　_____

　　　　_____　　**1**

　　(*b*)　The sulphur can be removed from compounds found in natural gas by reacting the compounds with hydrogen gas.

　　　　(i)　The equation for the removal of sulphur from one compound is shown.

　　　　　　CH_3SH　　+　　H_2　　→　　C_2H_6　　+　　H_2S

　　　　　　Balance this equation.　　**1**

　　　　(ii)　The hydrogen sulphide produced can be reacted to form sulphur gas.　The sulphur gas is cooled and forms liquid sulphur.

　　　　　　At what temperature will sulphur gas change to liquid?

　　　　　　(You may wish to use page 3 of the data booklet.)

　　　　　　_____ °C　　**1**

　　　　　　　　　　　　　　(3)

[Turn over

Marks

2. In ammonia molecules, the atoms are held together by three covalent bonds.

    (*a*) What is a covalent bond?

    _____

    _____   1

    (*b*) The formula of ammonia is NH_3.

    Draw a diagram to show the **shape** of an ammonia molecule.

    1

    (*c*) Ammonia gas $NH_3(g)$, can be dissolved in water to form concentrated ammonia solution.

    Hydrogen chloride gas $HCl(g)$, can be dissolved in water to form concentrated hydrochloric acid.

    If both bottles are placed next to each other in a fume cupboard and the stoppers removed, both liquids evaporate and a white cloud is formed where the two gases meet.

    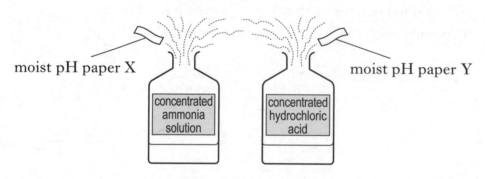

    (i) State the colour of the pH paper at X and Y.

    pH paper X _____   pH paper Y _____   1

    (ii) The white cloud appears because the gases react to form a salt. Name the salt formed.

    _____   1

(4)

Marks

3. The formula for iron(III) oxide is Fe_2O_3.

   (a) What is the charge on the oxide ion?
   (You may wish to use the data book to help you.)

   _____

   1

   (b) The iron(III) oxide can be reduced to give iron metal.
   Write an ion-electron equation to show iron(III) ions changing to iron atoms.

   _____

   1

   (c) Complete the table to show the numbers of particles in the iron ion $^{56}_{26}Fe^{3+}$.

Type of particle	Number
Protons	
Neutrons	
Electrons	

   2

   (4)

   [Turn over

Marks

4. In the **PPA "Effect of Temperature Changes on Reaction Rate"**, the rate of reaction between sodium thiosulphate and hydrochloric acid was investigated.

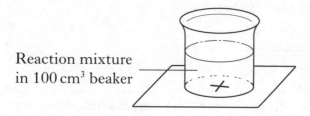

Reaction mixture
in 100 cm³ beaker

$$S_2O_3^{2-}(aq) \ + \ 2H^+(aq) \ \rightarrow \ SO_2(g) \ + \ S(s) \ + \ H_2O(\ell)$$

(a) Describe the change that would take place in the beaker.

_____

_____

1

(b) The results obtained during this PPA are shown in the table.

Temperature (°C)	Reaction time (s)	Relative rate 1/t (s⁻¹)
24	68	0·015
33	43	0·023
40	28	0·036
50	15	0·067

Plot these results as a line graph.

(Additional graph paper, if required, can be found on page 24).

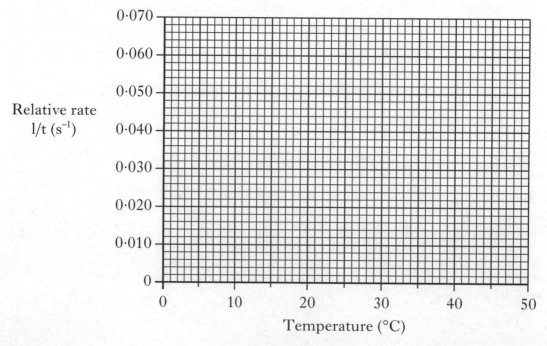

Relative rate
1/t (s⁻¹)

Temperature (°C)

1

Marks

4. **(continued)**

   (*c*)   (i) Use the graph to find the relative rate that would be expected if the reaction was carried out at 45 °C.

          _____ s^{-1}

                                                                            1

       (ii) At 60 °C the relative rate was $0{\cdot}125\,s^{-1}$. Use this rate to calculate the reaction time at 60 °C.

          _____ seconds

                                                                           1

   (*d*) When the experiment was carried out at the different temperatures, either the same beaker or identical beakers had to be used. Why is it important to use the same or identical beakers in this experiment?

    _____

    _____   **1**

                                                                          (5)

[Turn over

DO N
WRIT
TH
MAR(

Marks

5. Ethanoic acid is a member of the family of alkanoic acids.

(*a*) The functional group in ethanoic acid has been highlighted.

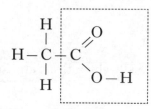

Name the functional group.

_____ 1

(*b*) Ethanoic acid can be produced by reacting methanol with carbon monoxide.

$$CH_3OH(\ell) \ + \ CO(g) \ \longrightarrow \ CH_3COOH(\ell)$$

Calculate the mass of ethanoic acid produced from 16 grams of methanol.

_____ g   2

(3)

Marks

6. Carbohydrates are an essential part of our diet.

  (*a*) Why are carbohydrates an important part of our diet?

_____

_____   **1**

  (*b*) Name the elements present in carbohydrates.

_____   **1**

  (*c*) A student tested the carbohydrates **glucose**, **sucrose** and **starch** as shown.

Test 1   **Test 2**

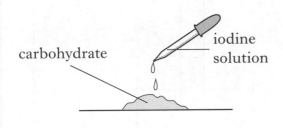
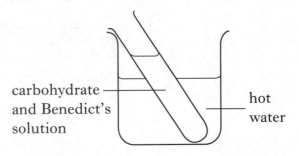

Complete the table by identifying each carbohydrate.

Carbohydrate	Results	
	Test 1	Test 2
	brown → black	no change
	no change	no change
	no change	blue → orange/red

2

(4)

[Turn over

Marks

7. (a) Draw the full structural formula for ethanol.

1

(b) The dehydration of ethanol to ethene was carried out using the following apparatus.

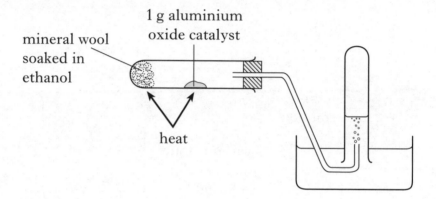

1 g aluminium oxide catalyst

mineral wool soaked in ethanol

heat

(i) Complete the word equation for the reaction.

Ethanol → Ethene + _____

1

(ii) As a safety precaution, the delivery tube was removed from the water before heating was stopped.
Why was this done?

_____

_____

1

(iii) Why is the aluminium oxide catalyst described as being heterogenous?

_____

_____

1

(iv) What would the mass of aluminium oxide catalyst be after the reaction was complete?

_____

1

(5)

Marks

8. Methylpropene and an alkane can be used to produce 2,2,4-trimethylpentane, a molecule added to petrol.

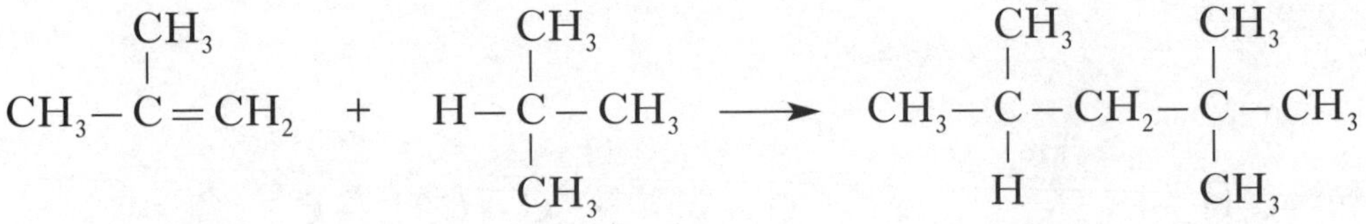

$$CH_3-\overset{\overset{\displaystyle CH_3}{|}}{C}=CH_2 \quad + \quad H-\overset{\overset{\displaystyle CH_3}{|}}{\underset{\underset{\displaystyle CH_3}{|}}{C}}-CH_3 \quad \longrightarrow \quad CH_3-\overset{\overset{\displaystyle CH_3}{|}}{\underset{\underset{\displaystyle H}{|}}{C}}-CH_2-\overset{\overset{\displaystyle CH_3}{|}}{\underset{\underset{\displaystyle CH_3}{|}}{C}}-CH_3$$

methylpropene   alkane   2,2,4-trimethylpentane

(a) (i) Give the systematic name for the alkane used to produce 2,2,4-trimethylpentane.

_____

1

(ii) Name the type of chemical reaction shown above.

_____

1

(b) A similar reaction can be used to prepare 2,2-dimethylpentane.
Draw a structural formula for the alkene used to form this molecule.

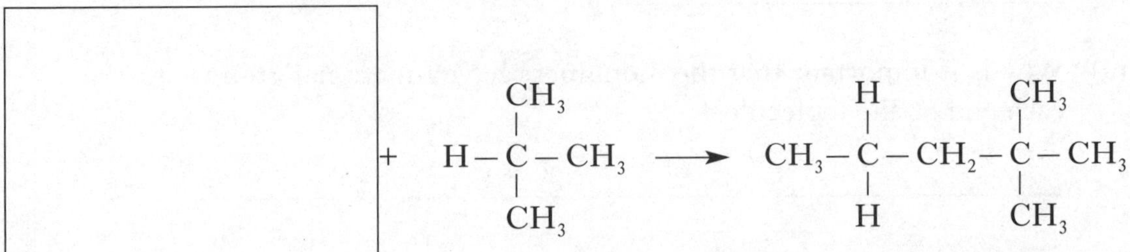

$$\boxed{} \quad + \quad H-\overset{\overset{\displaystyle CH_3}{|}}{\underset{\underset{\displaystyle CH_3}{|}}{C}}-CH_3 \quad \longrightarrow \quad CH_3-\overset{\overset{\displaystyle H}{|}}{\underset{\underset{\displaystyle H}{|}}{C}}-CH_2-\overset{\overset{\displaystyle CH_3}{|}}{\underset{\underset{\displaystyle CH_3}{|}}{C}}-CH_3$$

2,2-dimethylpentane

1

(3)

[Turn over

Marks

9. Kevlar is a thermosetting polymer which can be used to make bullet-proof vests.

(a) The diagram below shows how the monomers used to make Kevlar link together.

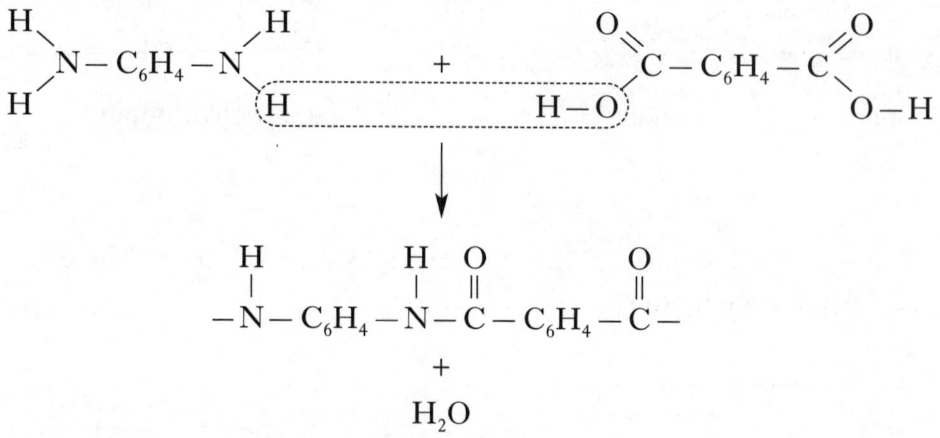

$$\underset{H}{\overset{H}{>}}N - C_6H_4 - N\overset{H}{\underset{H}{<}} \quad + \quad \overset{O}{\underset{H-O}{>}}C - C_6H_4 - C\overset{O}{\underset{O-H}{<}}$$

$$\downarrow$$

$$-\overset{H}{\underset{|}{N}} - C_6H_4 - \overset{H}{\underset{|}{N}} - \overset{O}{\underset{||}{C}} - C_6H_4 - \overset{O}{\underset{||}{C}} -$$

$$+$$

$$H_2O$$

(i) What type of polymerisation takes place?

_____   1

(ii) Name the type of link formed.

_____   1

(iii) Why is it important that the monomers have functional groups at each end of the molecule?

_____

_____

_____   1

(b) What property of Kevlar makes it suitable for use in bullet-proof vests?

_____

_____   1

(4)

Marks

10. The **PPA "Reactions of Metals with Oxygen"** was carried out using the apparatus shown below.

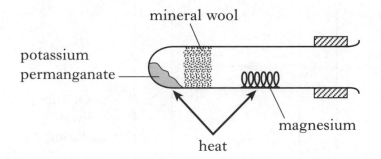

Three metals were used.

(*a*) Complete the table to show what would be observed when zinc was used.

Metal	Observation
Copper	Dull red glow
Magnesium	Very bright white light
Zinc	

1

(*b*) Complete the aim of the experiment.

The aim of the experiment was to _____

_____

_____   1

(*c*) Two safety precautions are wearing safety glasses and making sure the mouth of the test tube is not pointing at anyone.

State **one** other safety precaution which must be taken when using magnesium.

_____

_____   1

(3)

[Turn over

DO N
WRITE
TH
MARG

Marks

11. A student carried out the following experiment.

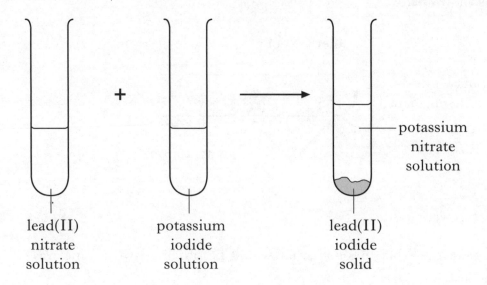

lead(II)   potassium   lead(II)
nitrate   iodide   iodide
solution   solution   solid

potassium
nitrate
solution

(a) During the reaction, a solid was formed.
   Name the type of chemical reaction taking place.

_____   1

(b) The equation for the reaction is

$$Pb^{2+}(aq) + 2NO_3^-(aq) + 2K^+(aq) + 2I^-(aq) \rightarrow Pb^{2+}(I^-)_2(s) + 2K^+(aq) + 2NO_3^-(aq)$$

   (i) Rewrite the equation showing only the ions which react.

   1

   (ii) What term is used to describe the ions which do not react?

   _____   1

   (3)

Marks

12. Scientists have developed self-heating food packs. They use the heat given out by the reaction of magnesium with water to warm food.

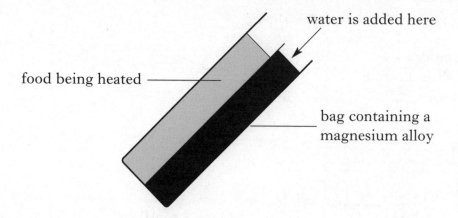

water is added here

food being heated

bag containing a
magnesium alloy

(a) What term is used to describe reactions which give out heat?

_____   1

(b) The reaction is started by the addition of water to the pouch containing magnesium alloy. The equation for the reaction is shown.

$$Mg(s) + 2H_2O(\ell) \longrightarrow Mg(OH)_2(s) + H_2(g)$$

(i) Why is it necessary to keep the food bag away from flames when the food is being heated?

_____

_____   1

(ii) In this reaction, magnesium atoms lose electrons.

$$Mg(s) \longrightarrow Mg^{2+}(aq) + 2e^-$$

What name is given to this type of chemical reaction?

_____   1

(c) In the alloy, magnesium is in contact with iron. This contact speeds up the reaction and produces heat more quickly.

Suggest why the magnesium being in contact with iron speeds up the reaction.

_____

_____   1

                                                                    (4)

[Turn over

Marks

13. Some medicines are made into tablets which fizz when they dissolve in water. The fizzing is caused by carbon dioxide gas which is produced when citric acid and sodium hydrogencarbonate in the tablet react.

The reaction can be demonstrated as shown.

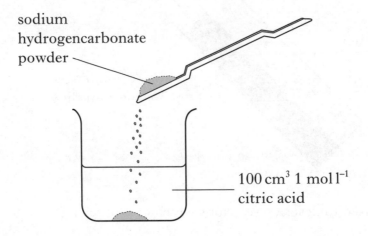

sodium hydrogencarbonate powder

$100 \, cm^3 \, 1 \, mol \, l^{-1}$ citric acid

(*a*) (i) Calculate the number of moles of citric acid in $100 \, cm^3$ of $1 \, mol \, l^{-1}$ citric acid.

_____ mol   **1**

(ii) 1 mole of citric acid reacts with 3 moles of sodium hydrogencarbonate.

How many moles of sodium hydrogencarbonate react with $100 \, cm^3$ of $1 \, mol \, l^{-1}$ citric acid?

_____ mol   **1**

DO NOT WRITE IN THIS MARGIN

Marks

13. (continued)

(*b*) (i) Citric acid is a weak acid.

What is meant by a weak acid?

____

____

____ **1**

(ii) Hydrochloric acid is a strong acid.

A student was given a bottle of 1 $mol\,l^{-1}$ hydrochloric acid and a bottle of 1 $mol\,l^{-1}$ citric acid.

Describe an experiment that could be carried out to show that citric acid is a weak acid and hydrochloric acid is a strong acid.

State the result that would be expected.

____

____

____

____

____

____

____ **2**

(5)

[*END OF QUESTION PAPER*]

DO N
WRIT
TH
MAR

ADDITIONAL SPACE FOR ANSWERS

ADDITIONAL GRAPH PAPER FOR QUESTION 4(*b*)

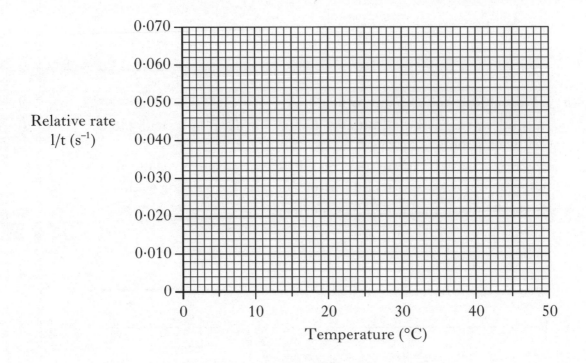

ADDITIONAL SPACE FOR ANSWERS

DO N
WRITE
THI
MARC

ADDITIONAL SPACE FOR ANSWERS

DO N
WRITE
THI
MARC

2007

[BLANK PAGE]

FOR OFFICIAL USE

Section B   **Total Marks**

X012/201

NATIONAL
QUALIFICATIONS
2007

TUESDAY, 29 MAY
9.00 AM – 11.00 AM

CHEMISTRY
INTERMEDIATE 2

Fill in these boxes and read what is printed below.

Full name of centre

Town

Forename(s)

Surname

Date of birth
Day Month Year   Scottish candidate number   Number of seat

Necessary data will be found in the Chemistry Data Booklet for Standard Grade and Intermediate 2.

Section A – Questions 1–30 (30 marks)

Instructions for completion of **Section A** are given on page two.

For this section of the examination you must use an **HB pencil**.

Section B (50 marks)

All questions should be attempted.

The questions may be answered in any order but all answers are to be written in the spaces provided in this answer book, **and must be written clearly and legibly in ink**.

Rough work, if any should be necessary, should be written in this book, and then scored through when the fair copy has been written. If further space is required, a supplementary sheet for rough work may be obtained from the invigilator.

Additional space for answers will be found at the end of the book. If further space is required, supplementary sheets may be obtained from the invigilator and should be inserted inside the **front** cover of this booklet.

Before leaving the examination room you must give this book to the invigilator. If you do not, you may lose all the marks for this paper.

SCOTTISH
QUALIFICATIONS
AUTHORITY

Read carefully

1 Check that the answer sheet provided is for **Chemistry Intermediate 2 (Section A)**.

2 For this section of the examination you must use an **HB pencil** and, where necessary, an eraser.

3 Check that the answer sheet you have been given has **your name**, **date of birth**, **SCN** (Scottish Candidate Number) and **Centre Name** printed on it.

   Do not change any of these details.

4 If any of this information is wrong, tell the Invigilator immediately.

5 If this information is correct, **print** your name and seat number in the boxes provided.

6 The answer to each question is **either** A, B, C or D. Decide what your answer is, then, using your pencil, put a horizontal line in the space provided (see sample question below).

7 There is **only one correct** answer to each question.

8 Any rough working should be done on the question paper or the rough working sheet, **not** on your answer sheet.

9 At the end of the exam, put the **answer sheet for Section A inside the front cover of this answer book**.

Sample Question

To show that the ink in a ball-pen consists of a mixture of dyes, the method of separation would be

   A   chromatography

   B   fractional distillation

   C   fractional crystallisation

   D   filtration.

The correct answer is **A**—chromatography. The answer **A** has been clearly marked in **pencil** with a horizontal line (see below).

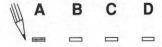

Changing an answer

If you decide to change your answer, carefully erase your first answer and using your pencil, fill in the answer you want. The answer below has been changed to **D**.

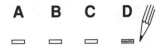

SECTION A

1. Which of the following elements has similar chemical properties to argon?

   A   Fluorine

   B   Krypton

   C   Potassium

   D   Zinc

2.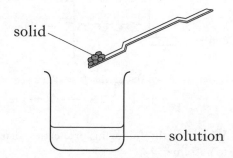

   Which of the following would **not** be evidence of a chemical reaction when the solid is added to the solution?

   A   A colour change

   B   A gas being given off

   C   The temperature rising

   D   The solid disappearing

3. Which line in the table shows the approximate percentage composition of air?

	Nitrogen	Oxygen	Carbon dioxide	Noble gases
A	78	21	0·03	1
B	21	78	1	0·03
C	1	21	78	0·03
D	0·03	78	1	21

4. Isotopes of the same element have identical

   A   nuclei

   B   mass numbers

   C   numbers of neutrons

   D   numbers of protons.

5. Vinegar is prepared by dissolving ethanoic acid in water.

   Which line in the table identifies the solute, solvent and solution?

	Solute	Solvent	Solution
A	water	ethanoic acid	vinegar
B	water	vinegar	ethanoic acid
C	ethanoic acid	water	vinegar
D	vinegar	water	ethanoic acid

6. Which of the following diagrams could be used to represent the structure of a covalent network compound?

   A

   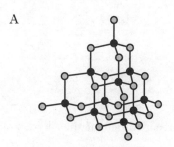

   B

   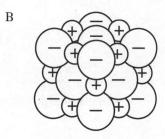

   C

   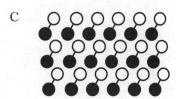

   D

   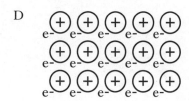

[Turn over

7. The table shows the colours of some ionic compounds in solution.

Compound	Colour
potassium chloride	colourless
potassium chromate	yellow
copper chromate	green
copper sulphate	blue

The colour of the chromate ion is

A   colourless

B   yellow

C   green

D   blue.

8. Gasoline produced by the fractional distillation of crude oil has a low viscosity.

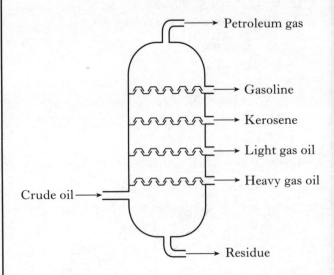

Which of the following properties also applies to gasoline?

A   High boiling point and high flammability

B   Low boiling point and high flammability

C   High boiling point and low flammability

D   Low boiling point and low flammability

9. The first three members of the alkyne homologous series are:

$$H-C\equiv C-H \qquad H-C\equiv C-\overset{\displaystyle H}{\underset{\displaystyle H}{\overset{|}{\underset{|}{C}}}}-H \qquad H-C\equiv C-\overset{\displaystyle H}{\underset{\displaystyle H}{\overset{|}{\underset{|}{C}}}}-\overset{\displaystyle H}{\underset{\displaystyle H}{\overset{|}{\underset{|}{C}}}}-H$$

What is the general formula for this homologous series?

A C_nH_n

B C_nH_{n+1}

C C_nH_{n+2}

D C_nH_{2n-2}

10.

```
      H   H   H   H
      |   |   |   |
  H — C — C — C — C — H
      |   |   |   |
      H   H   OH  H
```

Which of the following compounds is an isomer of the one above?

A

```
      H   H   H
      |   |   |
  H — C — C — C — H
      |   |   |
      H   H   OH
```

B

```
              H
              |
          H — C — H
      H   H   |       H
      |   |   |       |
  H — C — C — C ——— C — H
      |   |   |       |
      H   H   OH      H
```

C

```
      H   OH  H   H
      |   |   |   |
  H — C — C — C — C — H
      |   |   |   |
      H   H   H   H
```

D

```
      H   H   H   H
      |   |   |   |
  H — C — C — C — C — H
      |   |   |   |
      H   H   H   OH
```

11. Which of the following represents an ester?

A

```
      H           O
      |          ⫽      H
  H — C — C               |
      |          ＼ O — C — H
      H                   |
                          H
```

B

```
      H   H       H
      |   |       |
  H — C — C — O — C — H
      |   |       |
      H   H       H
```

C

```
      H   H   H
      |   |   |
  H — C — C — C — O — H
      |   |   |
      H   H   H
```

D

```
      H   H       O
      |   |      ⫽
  H — C — C — C
      |   |      ＼
      H   H       O — H
```

[Turn over

12. A student tested some compounds. The results are given in the table.

Compound	pH of aqueous solution	Effect on bromine solution
H—C—C—C with H,H,H,H and =O, OH	4	no effect
H—C=C—C with H,H and =O, OH	4	decolourised
H—C—C—C—OH with H,H,H,H,H,H	7	no effect
H—C=C—C—OH with H,H,H,H	7	decolourised

Which line in the table below shows the correct results for the following compound?

$$H-C-C=C-C-C-OH$$

(with H atoms: C1 has 3 H, C4 has 2 H, C5 has 2 H, OH group)

	pH of aqueous solution	Effect on bromine solution
A	4	decolourised
B	7	decolourised
C	4	no effect
D	7	no effect

13. Poly(ethenol) is

A a natural polymer, which is insoluble in water

B a natural polymer, which is soluble in water

C a synthetic polymer, which is soluble in water

D a synthetic polymer, which is insoluble in water.

14. Part of the structure of a polymer is drawn below.

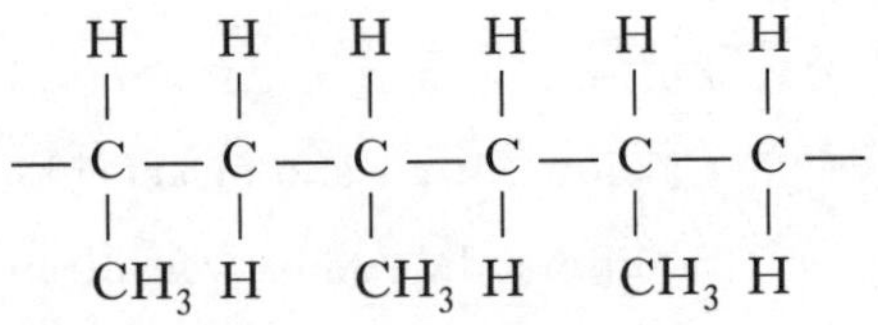

$$
\begin{array}{cccccc}
H & H & H & H & H & H \\
| & | & | & | & | & | \\
-C- & C- & C- & C- & C- & C- \\
| & | & | & | & | & | \\
CH_3 & H & CH_3 & H & CH_3 & H
\end{array}
$$

The repeating unit of this polymer is

A
$$
\begin{array}{c}
H \quad\quad CH_3 \\
\searrow \quad \nearrow \\
C = C \\
\nearrow \quad\quad \searrow \\
H_3C \quad\quad H
\end{array}
$$

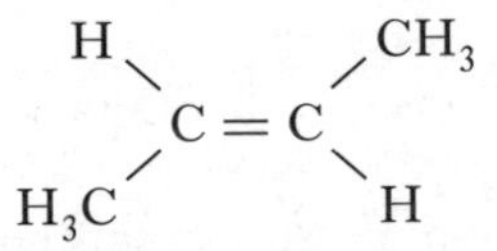

B
$$
\begin{array}{c}
H \quad\quad H \\
\searrow \quad \nearrow \\
-C - C- \\
\nearrow \quad\quad \searrow \\
H_3C \quad\quad H
\end{array}
$$

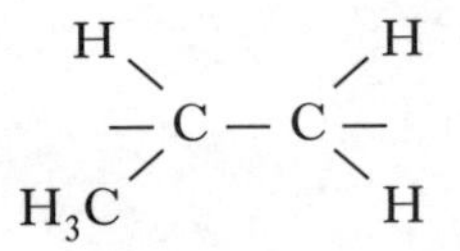

C
$$
\begin{array}{c}
H \quad\quad CH_2CH_3 \\
\searrow \quad \nearrow \\
C = C \\
\nearrow \quad\quad \searrow \\
H \quad\quad H
\end{array}
$$

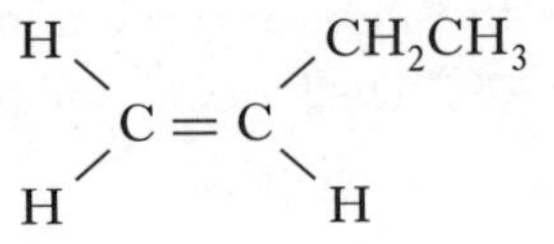

D
$$
\begin{array}{c}
H \quad\quad CH_2CH_3 \\
\searrow \quad \nearrow \\
-C - C- \\
\nearrow \quad\quad \searrow \\
H \quad\quad H
\end{array}
$$

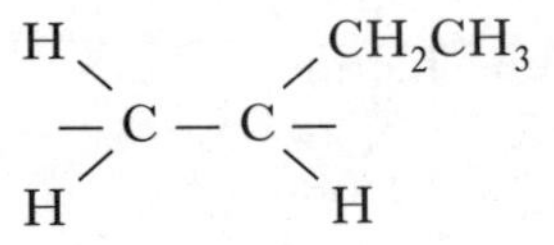

15. Which sugar will **not** be detected by the Benedict's test?

A Fructose

B Glucose

C Maltose

D Sucrose

16. The structure of glycerol is

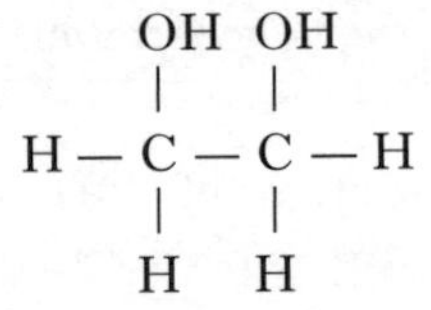

A
$$
\begin{array}{c}
OH \\
| \\
H-C-H \\
| \\
H
\end{array}
$$

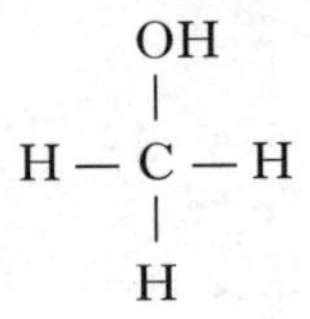

B
$$
\begin{array}{c}
OH \quad OH \\
| \quad\quad | \\
H-C-C-H \\
| \quad\quad | \\
H \quad\quad H
\end{array}
$$

C
$$
\begin{array}{c}
OH \quad OH \quad OH \\
| \quad\quad | \quad\quad | \\
H-C-C-C-H \\
| \quad\quad | \quad\quad | \\
H \quad\quad H \quad\quad H
\end{array}
$$

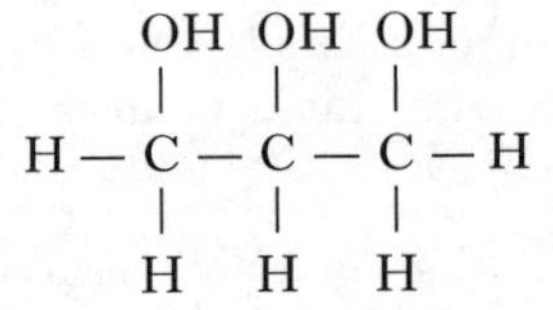

D
$$
\begin{array}{c}
OH \quad OH \quad OH \quad OH \\
| \quad\quad | \quad\quad | \quad\quad | \\
H-C-C-C-C-H \\
| \quad\quad | \quad\quad | \quad\quad | \\
H \quad\quad H \quad\quad H \quad\quad H
\end{array}
$$

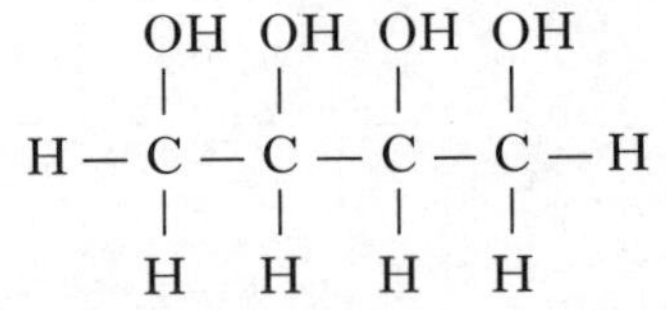

17. The conversion of an oil into a hardened fat involves the

A removal of hydrogen

B addition of hydrogen

C removal of water

D addition of water.

18. Which of the following oxides, when shaken with water, would leave the pH unchanged?

(You may wish to use page 5 of the data booklet to help you.)

A Carbon dioxide

B Copper oxide

C Sodium oxide

D Sulphur dioxide

19. Which of the following **increases** when hydrochloric acid is diluted with water?

A Rate of reaction with magnesium

B Concentration of H^+ ions

C Electrical conductivity

D pH

20. Which of the following statements describes the concentrations of $H^+(aq)$ and $OH^-(aq)$ ions in pure water?

A   The concentrations of $H^+(aq)$ and $OH^-(aq)$ ions are equal.

B   The concentrations of $H^+(aq)$ and $OH^-(aq)$ ions are zero.

C   The concentration of $H^+(aq)$ ions is greater than the concentration of $OH^-(aq)$ ions.

D   The concentration of $OH^-(aq)$ ions is greater than the concentration of $H^+(aq)$ ions.

21. When $100\,cm^3$ of a $1\,mol\,l^{-1}$ solution of sodium sulphate was evaporated to dryness, $14\cdot2\,g$ of solid was obtained.

To obtain $14\cdot2\,g$ of solid from a $2\,mol\,l^{-1}$ solution of sodium sulphate the volume of solution needed would be

A $25\,cm^3$

B $50\,cm^3$

C $100\,cm^3$

D $200\,cm^3$.

22. In which of the following test tubes will a gas be produced?

A

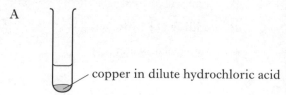

copper in dilute hydrochloric acid

B

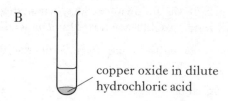

copper oxide in dilute hydrochloric acid

C

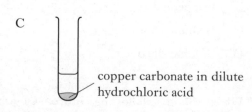

copper carbonate in dilute hydrochloric acid

D

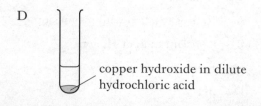

copper hydroxide in dilute hydrochloric acid

23. Which of the following compounds would **not** be used as a fertiliser?

A NH_4NO_3

B KNO_3

C $NaCl$

D K_3PO_4

24. Which of the following solutions would produce a precipitate when mixed together?

(You may wish to use page 5 of the data booklet to help you.)

A   Ammonium chloride and potassium nitrate

B   Zinc nitrate and magnesium sulphate

C   Calcium nitrate and nickel chloride

D   Sodium iodide and silver nitrate

25. Sodium sulphate solution reacts with barium chloride solution.

$$Na_2SO_4(aq) + BaCl_2(aq) \rightarrow BaSO_4(s) + 2NaCl(aq)$$

The spectator ions present in this reaction are

A Na^+ and Cl^-

B Na^+ and SO_4^{2-}

C Ba^{2+} and Cl^-

D Ba^{2+} and SO_4^{2-}.

26. Which of the following solutions will react with magnesium metal?

A   Magnesium chloride

B   Zinc chloride

C   Potassium chloride

D   Sodium chloride

27. Which of the following cells would produce the highest voltage?

(You may wish to use page 7 of the data booklet to help you.)

A

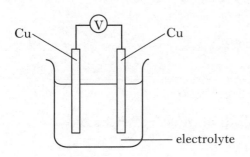

B

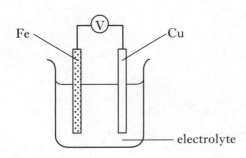

C

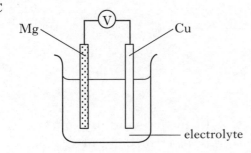

D

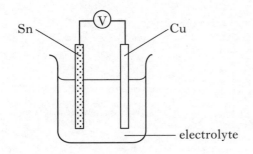

28.

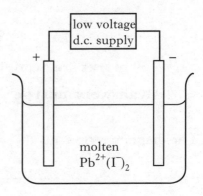

Which of the following describes the reaction at the positive electrode?

A　I^- reduced

B　I^- oxidised

C　Pb^{2+} oxidised

D　Pb^{2+} reduced

29. The table contains information about calcium and calcium chloride.

	Melting point (°C)	Density (g cm^{-3})
Calcium	842	1·54
Calcium chloride	772	2·15

When molten calcium chloride is electrolysed at 800 °C the calcium appears as a

A　solid on the surface of the molten calcium chloride

B　liquid on the surface of the molten calcium chloride

C　solid at the bottom of the molten calcium chloride

D　liquid at the bottom of the molten calcium chloride.

30. Which ion will turn ferroxyl indicator pink?

A　$Fe^{2+}(aq)$

B　$Fe^{3+}(aq)$

C　$H^+(aq)$

D　$OH^-(aq)$

Candidates are reminded that the answer sheet for Section A MUST be placed INSIDE the front cover of this answer book.

Marks

SECTION B

50 marks are available in this section of the paper.

All answers must be written clearly and legibly in ink.

1. The diagram represents the structure of an atom.

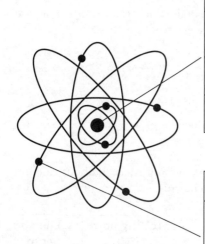

In the Nucleus		
Name of particle	Relative mass	Charge
Proton		+1
Neutron	1	

Outside the Nucleus		
Name of particle	Relative mass	Charge
	almost zero	

(a) Complete the tables.   2

(b) Ernest Rutherford used alpha particles to confirm the structure of the atom. The table shows the number of protons, electrons and neutrons in an alpha particle.

	Number
Proton	2
Electron	0
Neutron	2

(i) What is the atomic number of an alpha particle?

_____   1

Marks

1. (*b*) (continued)

   (ii) When alpha particles are passed through an electric field, which letter in the diagram shows the path taken by them?

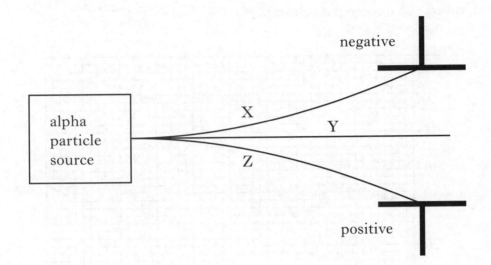

   Letter _____

1

(4)

[Turn over

DO N
WRIT
TH
MARC

Marks

2. Hydrogen peroxide solution decomposes to give water and oxygen.

$$2H_2O_2(aq) \rightarrow 2H_2O(\ell) + O_2(g)$$

(a) The graph shows the results of an experiment carried out to measure the volume of oxygen gas released.

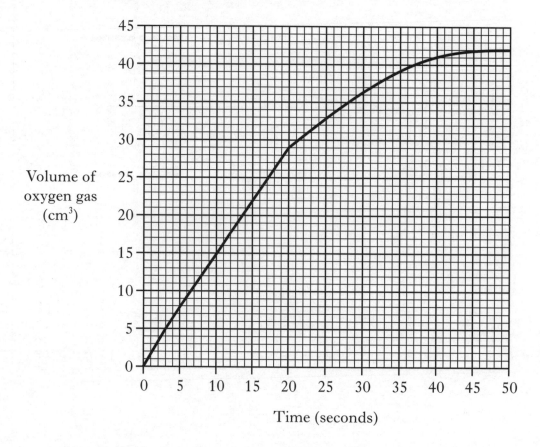

Time (seconds)

Calculate the average rate of reaction between 0 and 20 seconds.

_____ $cm^3 s^{-1}$ 1

(b) The reaction was catalysed by a **solution** of Fe^{3+} ions which is amber in colour.

(i) Why is the term homogeneous used to describe this catalyst?

_____

_____   1

(ii) What colour would the solution be at the end of the reaction?

_____   1

Marks

3. Tin and its compounds have many uses.

   (*a*) Why do metals such as tin conduct electricity?

   _____

   _____   1

   (*b*) Tin(IV) chloride, $SnCl_4$, is used in the processing of glass and can be prepared as shown.

   $$SnO_2 \ + \ 4HCl \ \rightarrow \ SnCl_4 \ + \ 2H_2O$$

   (i) Name the type of reaction taking place.

   _____   1

   (ii) Tin(IV) chloride is a liquid at room temperature and is made up of discrete molecules.

   What type of bonding does this suggest is present in tin(IV) chloride?

   _____   1

   (3)

   [Turn over

Marks

4. Magnesium reacts with dilute hydrochloric acid.

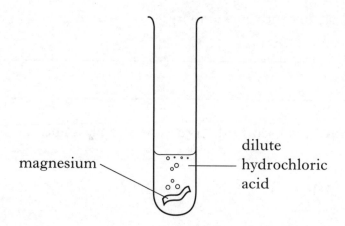

magnesium

dilute
hydrochloric
acid

The equation for the reaction is shown.

$$Mg(s) + 2HCl(aq) \rightarrow MgCl_2(\ ) + H_2(g)$$

(a) (i) Complete the equation by adding the state symbol for magnesium chloride.

(You may wish to use page 5 of the data booklet to help you.)   1

(ii) State the test for hydrogen gas.

_____   1

(b) In an experiment 4·9 g of magnesium reacted with excess dilute hydrochloric acid. Calculate the mass of hydrogen produced in this reaction.

_____ g   2

(4)

Marks

5. Thiols are organic compounds containing sulphur. Some thiols are listed in the table.

Formula	Name of thiol
CH_3SH	methanethiol
CH_3CH_2SH	ethanethiol
CH_3 | CH_3CHCH_2SH	**X**
CH_3 | $CH_3CHCH_2CH_2SH$	3-methylbutane-1-thiol

(a) Ethanethiol is added to natural gas to give it a smell.

Draw the **full** structural formula for ethanethiol.

1

(b) Suggest the name for thiol **X**.

_____

1

(c) Thiols undergo complete combustion.

thiols + oxygen → carbon dioxide + water + _____

Complete the word equation for this reaction.

1

(3)

[Turn over

DO N
WRIT
TH
MAR(

Marks

6. A student completed the **PPA "Testing for Unsaturation"**. Results from the experiment are shown in the table.

Hydrocarbon	Molecular formula	Observation with bromine solution	Saturated or unsaturated
A	C_6H_{14}	no change	
B	C_6H_{12}		unsaturated
C	C_6H_{12}		saturated
D	C_6H_{10}	bromine decolourises	

(a) Complete the table.

2

(b) Care had to be taken when using bromine solution. Give a safety precaution, **other** than eye protection, which should be taken when completing this PPA.

_____

1

(c) Suggest a possible name for hydrocarbon **B**.

_____

1

(4)

Marks

7. Polystyrene is made from the monomer, styrene. The systematic name for styrene is phenylethene.

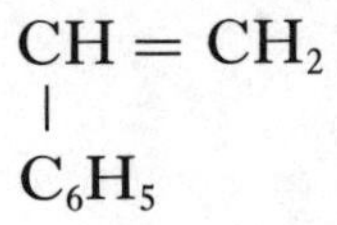

$$CH = CH_2$$
$$|$$
$$C_6H_5$$

Styrene (phenylethene)

(a) The monomer used to form polystyrene is shown.

Which part of the structure of styrene allows the polymer to form?

_____   1

(b) Complete the diagram to show how three styrene molecules join to form part of the polymer chain.

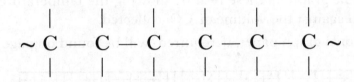

1

(c) Give another name for polystyrene.

_____   1

(3)

[Turn over

DO N
WRITE
THE
MARG

Marks

8. The fermentation of glucose is catalysed by the enzyme zymase.

$$C_6H_{12}O_6(aq) \quad \rightarrow \quad C_2H_5OH(aq) \quad + \quad CO_2(g)$$

(*a*) Balance the equation.

1

(*b*) A series of fermentation experiments was carried out at different temperatures and the volume of carbon dioxide was measured.

Experiment	Temperature (°C)	Volume of CO_2 (cm³)
1	15	8
2	20	25
3	25	35
4	30	42
5	35	27
6	40	14

(i) Plot a line graph of these results, showing the temperature of the reaction against the volume of CO_2 collected.

(Additional graph paper, if required, will be found on page 28.)

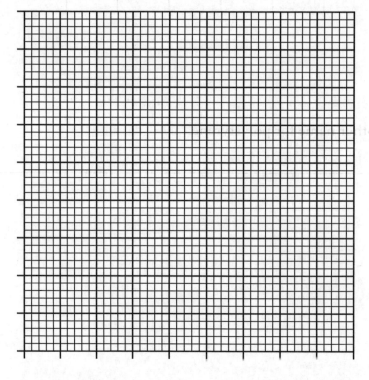

2

(ii) When the experiment was carried out at 70 °C, no carbon dioxide was produced.

Suggest a reason for this.

1

Marks

9. When a hydrocarbon is burnt, carbon dioxide and water are produced. The following experiment can be used to investigate the products of combustion.

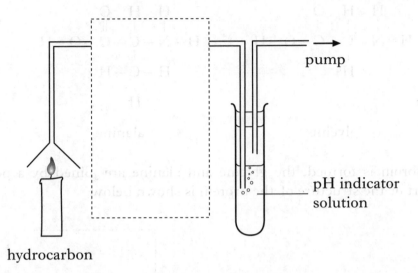

(a) Complete the diagram to show the apparatus which would be used to collect the water.

1

(b) When the carbon dioxide produced in the reaction is passed through the pH indicator solution, the solution turns from green to red.

What does this colour change suggest about carbon dioxide?

_____

1

(2)

[Turn over

Marks

10. The silk that spiders spin into a web is made from a protein called fibroin. Two of the amino acids spiders use to make this protein are glycine and alanine.

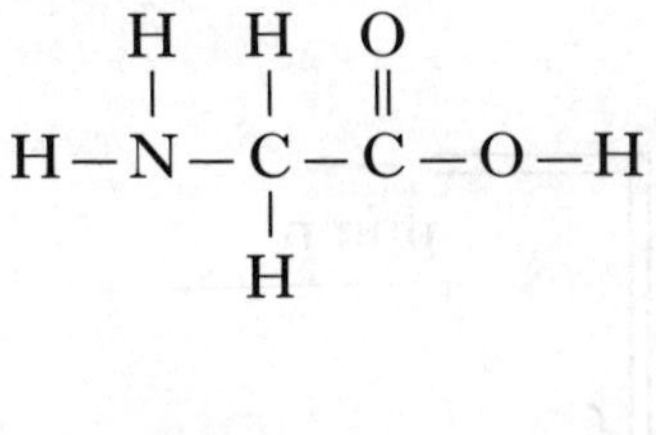

glycine 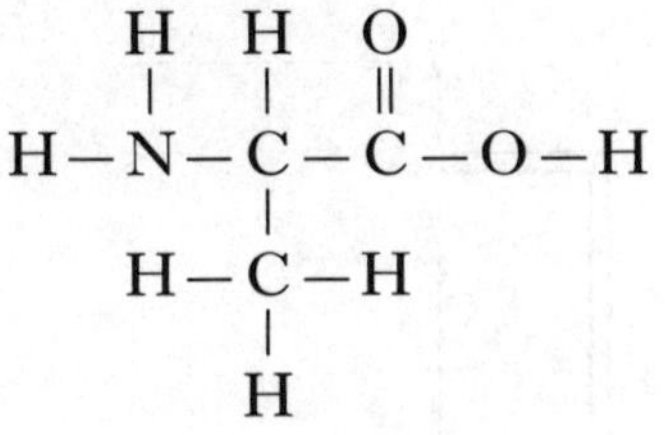   alanine

When fibroin is formed, the glycine and alanine are joined by a peptide link. Part of the structure of the protein is shown below.

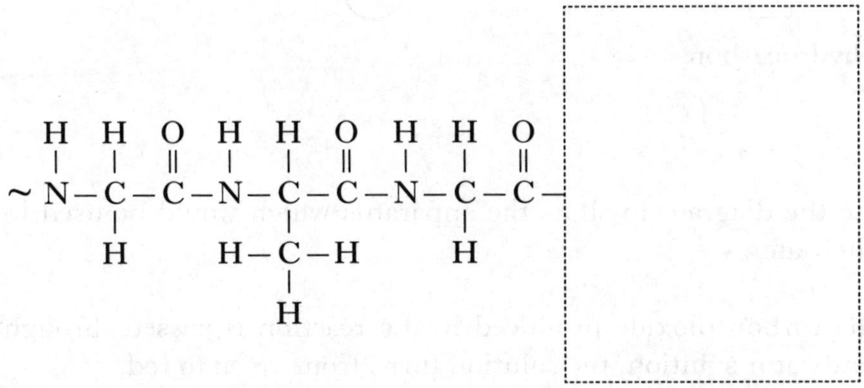

(a) Circle a peptide link in the protein structure.   1

(b) Complete the structure by adding another molecule of **glycine**.   1

(c) Name the type of polymerisation that produces fibroin.

_____   1

(3)

DO NOT
WRITE IN
THIS
MARGIN

Marks

11. The Statue of Liberty is made from copper attached to an iron frame.

Statue of Liberty

(a) Why does the iron frame rust more quickly when attached to the copper?

_____

_____

_____   1

(b) The statue sits on an island surrounded by seawater.
Why does the seawater increase the rate of rusting?

_____

_____

_____   1

(c) Rust contains iron(III) oxide.
Write the formula for iron(III) oxide.

_____   1

(3)

[Turn over

Marks

12. Electrolysis of molten sodium hydride produces hydrogen gas.

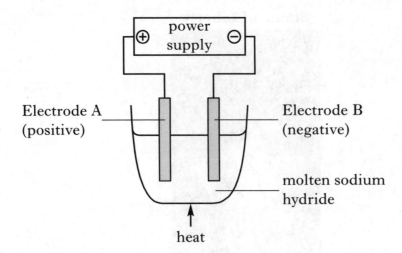

The ion-electron equations taking place at the electrodes are:

$$Na^+ + e^- \rightarrow Na$$

$$2H^- \rightarrow H_2 + 2e^-$$

(a) Use the equations to identify the electrode at which hydrogen gas is produced.

_____   1

(b) Combine the two ion-electron equations to give the **balanced** redox equation.

_____   1

(c) Sodium hydride reacts with water to form a solution of sodium hydroxide.

Sodium hydroxide is an example of a strong base.

Complete the table by circling the correct words to show how the properties of sodium hydroxide solution compare with ammonia solution, which is a weak base.

	0·1 mol l⁻¹ ammonia solution	0·1 mol l⁻¹ sodium hydroxide solution
pH	10	lower higher
Current in a conductivity cell (microamps)	22	lower higher

1

(3)

Marks

13.

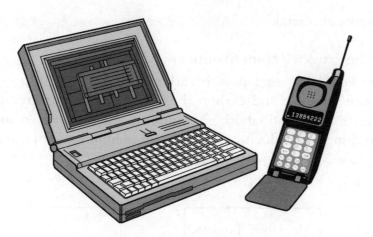

Lithium cells are used as batteries in laptops and mobile phones. In these cells lithium is present as ions.

(*a*)   (i)   Write the electron arrangement for the lithium **ion**.

1

      (ii)   Suggest an advantage of using lithium **ions** rather than lithium atoms in the cell.

_____   1

(*b*)   The voltages of cells can be measured. Some voltages of cells in which different metals are connected to copper are shown in the table.

Metal connected to copper	Voltage (V)
Iron	0·44
Lead	0·13
Lithium	3·02

State the relationship between the position of the metal in the electrochemical series and voltage.

_____   1

(3)

[Turn over

Marks

14. Titanium is an important metal.

(*a*) Titanium can be extracted from titanium dioxide.

The titanium dioxide is reacted with carbon and chlorine to produce impure titanium chloride and carbon dioxide. The impure titanium chloride is purified by distillation. Magnesium metal is added to the pure titanium chloride producing titanium and magnesium chloride.

Complete the flow chart to show the extraction process.

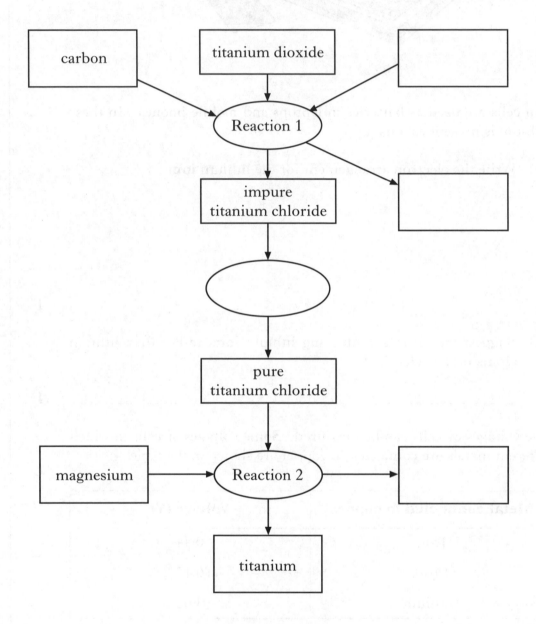

2

Marks

14.   **(continued)**

(b) A mixture of titanium and nickel is used to make the alloy, Nitinol.
This alloy is used to make dental braces.
The composition of Nitinol is shown in the table.

Metal	titanium	nickel
percentage by mass	45	55

A set of braces has a mass of 8 g.

(i) Calculate the mass of titanium in the braces.

_____ g   **1**

(ii) Calculate the number of moles of titanium in the braces.
(Relative atomic mass of titanium = 48)

_____   **1**

(4)

Marks

15. A student carried out a **PPA** to prepare the salt, magnesium sulphate.

(*a*) Name the acid used to make this salt.

_____   1

(*b*) Part of the student's PPA assessment sheet is shown.

Intermediate 2 Chemistry	Preparation of a Salt	Unit 3 PPA1

Assessment Sheet

Aim   To prepare magnesium sulphate crystals by reacting excess magnesium with dilute acid.

Procedure

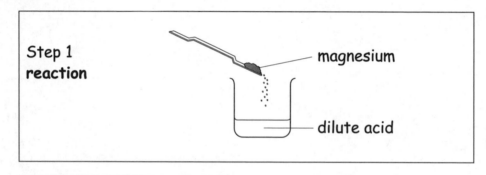

Step 1
reaction

magnesium

dilute acid

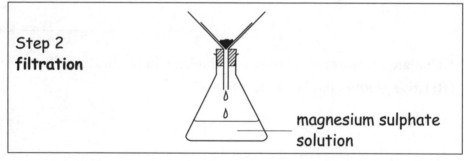

Step 2
filtration

magnesium sulphate solution

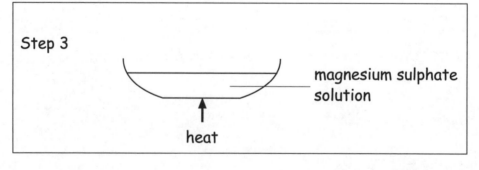

Step 3

magnesium sulphate solution

heat

Marks

15. (b) (continued)

(i) Why was the reaction mixture filtered in step 2?

_____   **1**

(ii) There are three steps in the preparation of magnesium sulphate.

Step 1   reaction

Step 2   filtration

Step 3 _____

Name step 3.   **1**

(c) The diagram shows the chemical energies of the reactants and products when magnesium reacts with dilute acid.

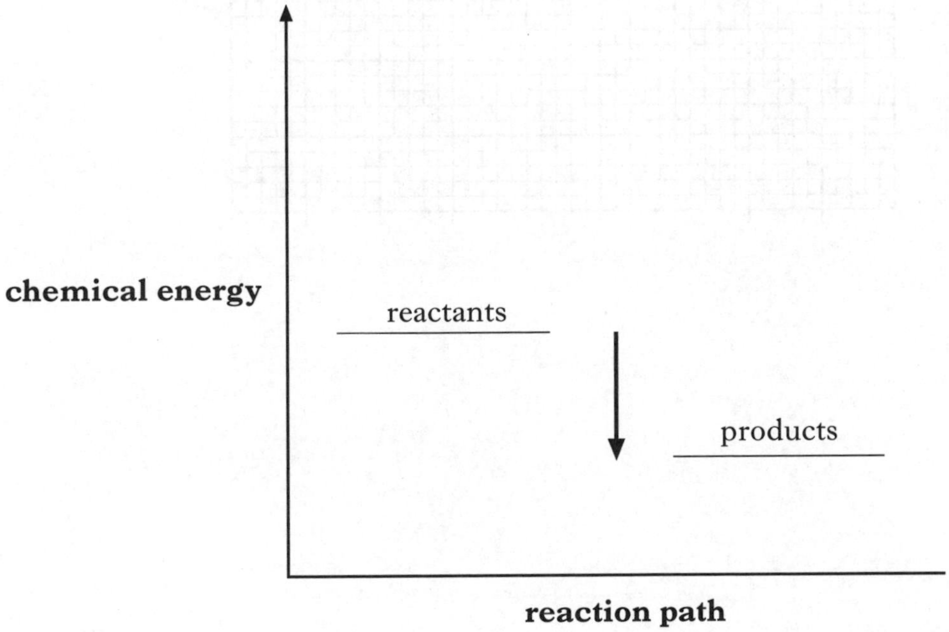

chemical energy

reactants

products

reaction path

In what way does the energy diagram show that the reaction is exothermic?

_____

_____

_____   **1**

(4)

[END OF QUESTION PAPER]

DO N
WRIT
TH
MAR

ADDITIONAL SPACE FOR ANSWERS

ADDITIONAL GRAPH PAPER FOR QUESTION 8(*b*)(i)

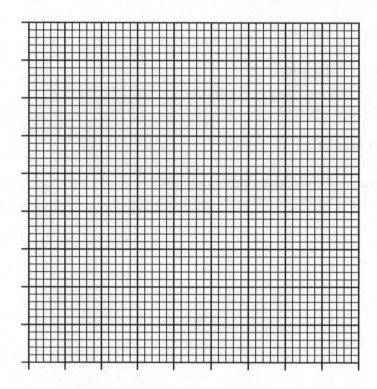

ADDITIONAL SPACE FOR ANSWERS

ADDITIONAL SPACE FOR ANSWERS

ADDITIONAL SPACE FOR ANSWERS

[BLANK PAGE]

2008

[BLANK PAGE]

FOR OFFICIAL USE

Section B   **Total Marks**

X012/201

NATIONAL
QUALIFICATIONS
2008

FRIDAY, 30 MAY
9.00 AM – 11.00 AM

CHEMISTRY
INTERMEDIATE 2

Fill in these boxes and read what is printed below.

Full name of centre

Town

Forename(s)

Surname

Date of birth
Day Month Year   Scottish candidate number   Number of seat

Necessary data will be found in the Chemistry Data Booklet for Standard Grade and Intermediate 2.

Section A – Questions 1–30 (30 marks)

Instructions for completion of **Section A** are given on page two.

For this section of the examination you must use an **HB pencil**.

Section B (50 marks)

All questions should be attempted.

The questions may be answered in any order but all answers are to be written in the spaces provided in this answer book, **and must be written clearly and legibly in ink**.

Rough work, if any should be necessary, should be written in this book, and then scored through when the fair copy has been written. If further space is required, a supplementary sheet for rough work may be obtained from the invigilator.

Additional space for answers will be found at the end of the book. If further space is required, supplementary sheets may be obtained from the invigilator and should be inserted inside the **front** cover of this booklet.

Before leaving the examination room you must give this book to the invigilator. If you do not, you may lose all the marks for this paper.

Read carefully

1 Check that the answer sheet provided is for **Chemistry Intermediate 2 (Section A)**.

2 For this section of the examination you must use an **HB pencil** and, where necessary, an eraser.

3 Check that the answer sheet you have been given has **your name**, **date of birth**, **SCN** (Scottish Candidate Number) and **Centre Name** printed on it.

   Do not change any of these details.

4 If any of this information is wrong, tell the Invigilator immediately.

5 If this information is correct, **print** your name and seat number in the boxes provided.

6 The answer to each question is **either** A, B, C or D. Decide what your answer is, then, using your pencil, put a horizontal line in the space provided (see sample question below).

7 There is **only one correct** answer to each question.

8 Any rough working should be done on the question paper or the rough working sheet, **not** on your answer sheet.

9 At the end of the exam, put the **answer sheet for Section A inside the front cover of this answer book**.

Sample Question

To show that the ink in a ball-pen consists of a mixture of dyes, the method of separation would be

        A chromatography

        B fractional distillation

        C fractional crystallisation

        D filtration.

The correct answer is **A**—chromatography. The answer **A** has been clearly marked in **pencil** with a horizontal line (see below).

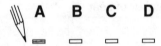

Changing an answer

If you decide to change your answer, carefully erase your first answer and using your pencil, fill in the answer you want. The answer below has been changed to **D**.

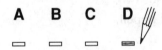

SECTION A

1. Which of the following pairs of reactants would produce hydrogen most slowly?

   A Magnesium powder and 4 mol l^{-1} acid

   B Magnesium ribbon and 2 mol l^{-1} acid

   C Magnesium powder and 2 mol l^{-1} acid

   D Magnesium ribbon and 4 mol l^{-1} acid

2. Vinegar can be made by dissolving ethanoic acid in water.

   Which term describes the water used when making the vinegar?

   A Solute

   B Saturated

   C Solvent

   D Solution

3. Which of the following is an element?

   A Ammonia

   B Carbon dioxide

   C Fluorine

   D Methane

4. An atom is neutral because

   A the number of electrons equals the total number of protons plus neutrons

   B the number of neutrons equals the total number of electrons plus protons

   C the number of protons equals the number of neutrons

   D the number of electrons equals the number of protons.

5. Which of the following is the electron arrangement for a noble gas?

   (You may wish to use page 1 of the data booklet to help you.)

   A 2, 5

   B 2, 6

   C 2, 7

   D 2, 8

6. The table shows information about an **ion**.

Particle	Number
protons	19
neutrons	20
electrons	18

   The charge on the ion is

   A 1+

   B 1–

   C 2+

   D 2–.

7. Which of the following diagrams could be used to represent the structure of a metal?

   A
   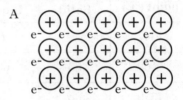

   B
   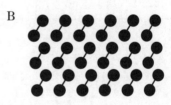

   C
   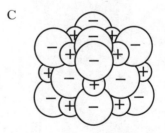

   D
   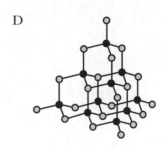

8. When methane burns in a plentiful supply of air, the products are

    A   carbon monoxide and water vapour

    B   carbon and water vapour

    C   carbon dioxide and hydrogen

    D   carbon dioxide and water vapour.

9. How many moles are present in $1.7\,g$ of ammonia, NH_3?

    A 0.1

    B 1.0

    C 1.7

    D 17

10. Which line in the table shows the properties of an ionic compound?

	Melting point (°C)	Boiling point (°C)	Conducts electricity?	
			Solid	Liquid
A	181	1347	yes	yes
B	−95	69	no	no
C	686	1330	no	yes
D	1700	2230	no	no

11. The fractional distillation of crude oil produces a number of different fractions.

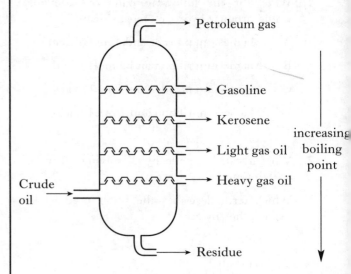

Compared with the gasoline fraction, the heavy gas oil fraction is

    A   less viscous and evaporates more readily

    B   more viscous and evaporates more readily

    C   less viscous and evaporates less readily

    D   more viscous and evaporates less readily.

12.

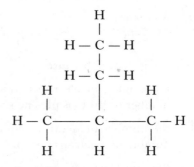

The name of the above compound is

    A   1, 1–dimethylpropane

    B   2-ethylpropane

    C   2-methylbutane

    D   3-methylbutane.

13. Which of the following compounds fits the general formula, C_nH_{2n}, and will rapidly decolourise bromine solution?

    A   Cyclopentane

    B   Cyclopentene

    C   Pentane

    D   Pentene

14. Three members of the cycloalkene homologous series are:

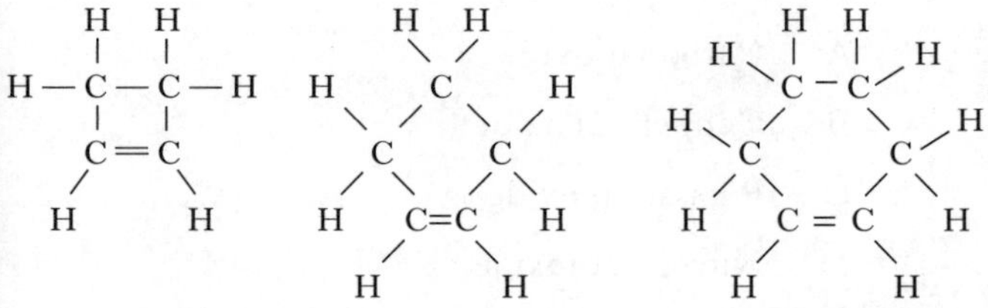

H—C—C—H   (structures shown)   (structures shown)

The general formula for this homologous series is

A C_nH_{2n+2}

B C_nH_{2n}

C C_nH_{2n-2}

D C_nH_{2n-4}.

15. Which of the following molecules is an isomer of heptane?

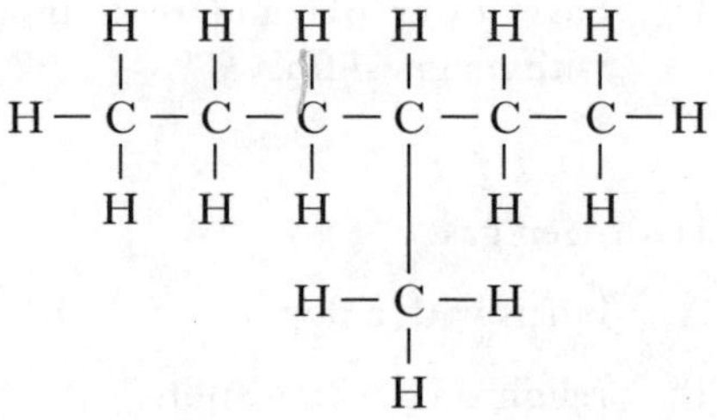

A

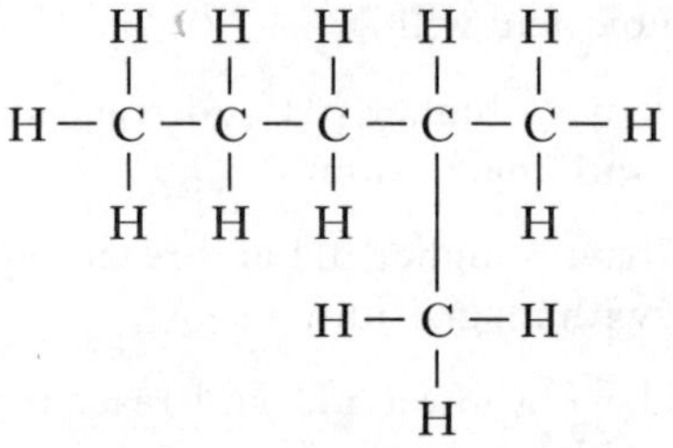

$$H-\overset{H}{\underset{H}{C}}-\overset{H}{\underset{H}{C}}-\overset{H}{\underset{H}{C}}-\overset{H}{\underset{|}{C}}-\overset{H}{\underset{H}{C}}-H$$

with $H-\overset{}{C}-H$ branch below

B

$$H-\overset{H}{\underset{H}{C}}-\overset{H}{\underset{H}{C}}-\overset{H}{\underset{H}{C}}-\overset{H}{\underset{|}{C}}-\overset{H}{\underset{H}{C}}-\overset{H}{\underset{H}{C}}-H$$

with $H-C-H$ branch below

C

with $H-C-H$ branch

$$H-C-C-C-C-C=C-H$$

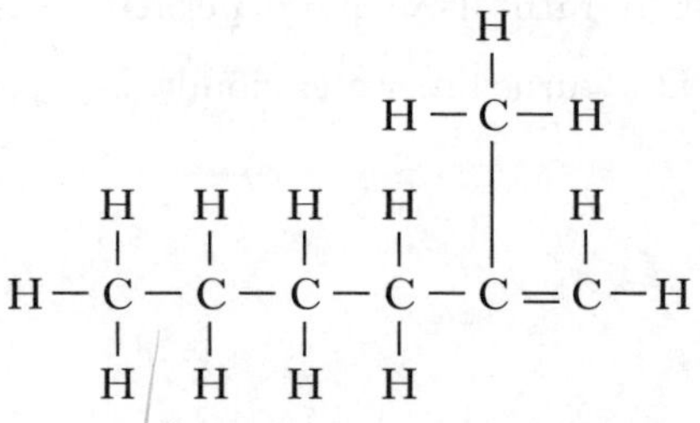

D

$$H-C-C-C-C-C=C-C-H$$

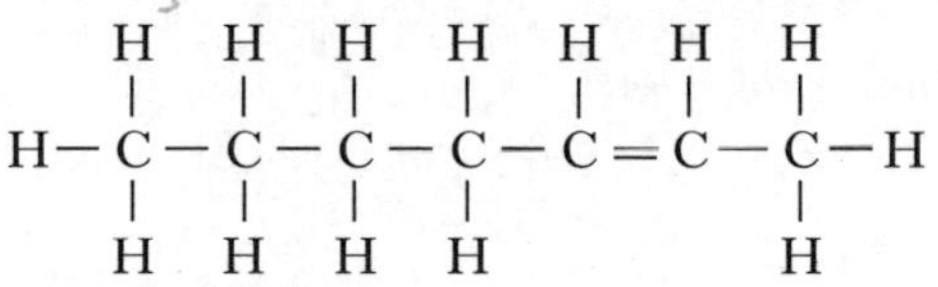

16. Fermentation of glucose to ethanol and carbon dioxide by yeast stops when the ethanol concentration reaches about 13%.

This is because

A   the ethanol has destroyed the yeast

B   all the glucose has been used up

C   carbon dioxide is harmful to yeast

D   the mixture is now saturated with ethanol.

17.

methanol + ethanoic acid → methyl ethanoate + water

This reaction is an example of

A   addition

B   dehydration

C   condensation

D   neutralisation.

18. The flow diagram shows the manufacture of polythene from hydrocarbons in crude oil.

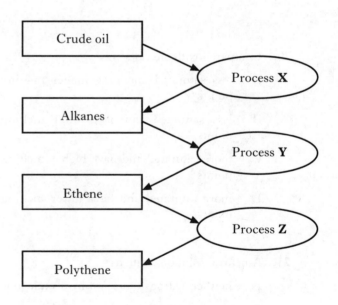

Which line in the table identifies processes **X**, **Y** and **Z**?

	Process X	Process Y	Process Z
A	distillation	cracking	hydrolysis
B	cracking	combustion	polymerisation
C	polymerisation	distillation	hydrolysis
D	distillation	cracking	polymerisation

19. Which of the following structures is that of an amino acid?

A

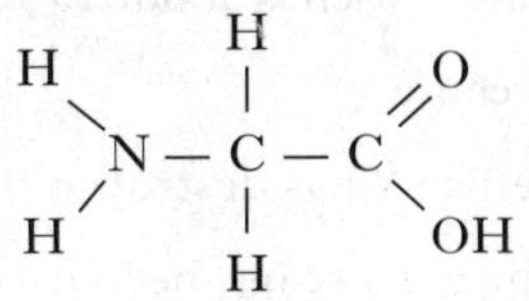

B

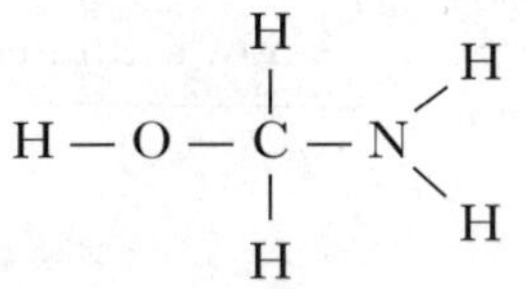

C

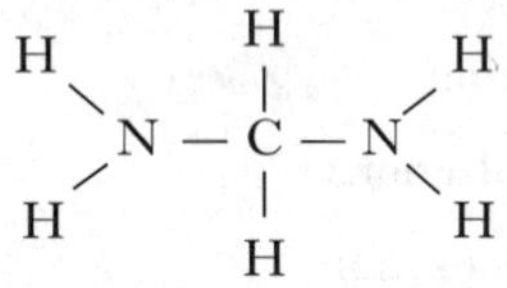

D

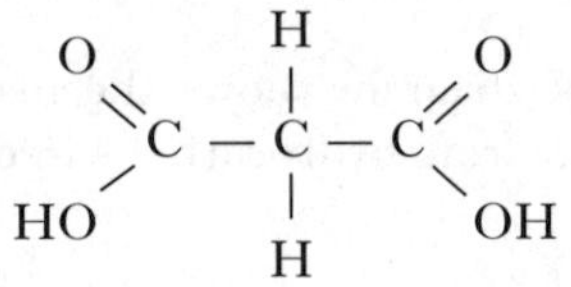

20. Compared with oils, fats are

A   less saturated and have higher melting points

B   less saturated and have lower melting points

C   more saturated and have higher melting points

D   more saturated and have lower melting points.

21. A neutral solution contains

A   neither hydrogen ions nor hydroxide ions

B   equal numbers of hydrogen ions and hydroxide ions

C   more hydrogen ions than hydroxide ions

D   more hydroxide ions than hydrogen ions.

22. Which of the following oxides will dissolve in water to produce an alkaline solution?

(You may wish to use page 5 of the data booklet to help you.)

A   Carbon dioxide

B   Copper(II) oxide

C   Potassium oxide

D   Nitrogen dioxide

23. 1 mole of sodium chloride can be used to prepare

A $250\,cm^3$ of a $0{\cdot}4\,mol\,l^{-1}$ solution

B $250\,cm^3$ of a $4\,mol\,l^{-1}$ solution

C $200\,cm^3$ of a $0{\cdot}5\,mol\,l^{-1}$ solution

D $200\,cm^3$ of a $1\,mol\,l^{-1}$ solution.

24. Compared to a $1\,mol\,l^{-1}$ solution of hydrochloric acid, a $1\,mol\,l^{-1}$ solution of ethanoic acid will

A   have a higher pH and react more slowly with magnesium

B   have a higher pH and react more quickly with magnesium

C   have a lower pH and react more slowly with magnesium

D   have lower pH and react more quickly with magnesium.

25. Hydrogen gas

A   burns with a pop

B   relights a glowing splint

C   turns damp pH paper red

D   turns limewater cloudy.

26.

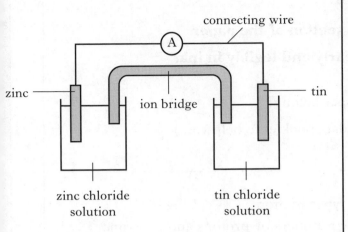

In the cell shown, electrons flow through

A   the solution from tin to zinc

B   the solution from zinc to tin

C   the connecting wire from tin to zinc

D   the connecting wire from zinc to tin.

27. Four cells were made by joining copper, iron, tin and zinc to silver. The voltages are shown in the table.

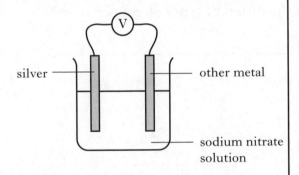

Which line in the table shows the voltage of the cell containing copper joined to silver?

(You may wish to use page 7 of the data booklet to help you.)

Cell	Voltage (V)
A	1·6
B	1·2
C	0·9
D	0·5

28. Which of the following metals is found uncombined in the Earth's crust?

A   Aluminium

B   Iron

C   Lead

D   Silver

29. Which ion gives a blue colour with ferroxyl indicator?

A H^+(aq)

B OH^-(aq)

C Fe^{2+}(aq)

D Fe^{3+}(aq)

30. Which of the following methods can give both physical and sacrificial protection to iron?

A   Painting

B   Greasing

C   Tin-plating

D   Galvanising

Candidates are reminded that the answer sheet for Section A MUST be placed INSIDE the front cover of this answer book.

DO N
WRITE
THI
MARC

Marks

SECTION B

50 marks are available in this section of the paper.

All answers must be written clearly and legibly in ink.

1. (*a*) To which family of metals does copper belong?

   (You may wish to use page 8 of the data booklet to help you.)

   _____   1

   (*b*) Copper is made up of two different types of atom.

   (i) Complete the table to show the numbers of protons and neutrons in each type of copper atom.

	Number of protons	Number of neutrons
$^{63}_{29}Cu$		
$^{65}_{29}Cu$		

   2

   (ii) What term is used to describe the different types of copper atom?

   _____   1

   (4)

Marks

2. The graph shows how the solubility of potassium chloride changes with temperature.

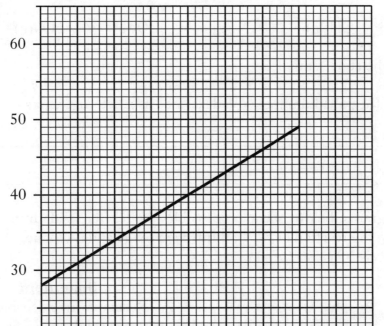

Solubility of potassium chloride (g per 100 cm^3 water)

Temperature of the water (°C)

(a) From the graph, what is the maximum mass of potassium chloride that will dissolve at 60 °C?

_____ g per 100cm^3 1

(b) The potassium chloride solution is cooled from 60 °C to 30 °C. A solid forms at the bottom of the beaker.

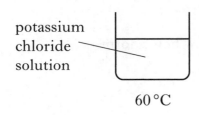

potassium chloride solution

60 °C

potassium chloride solution

30 °C

solid potassium chloride

(i) Using the graph, calculate the mass of solid potassium chloride formed at the bottom of the beaker at 30 °C.

_____ g   1

(ii) What method could be used to separate the solid which forms?

_____   1

(3)

DO N
WRITI
THI
MARC

Marks

3. When dinitrogen oxide, N_2O, is mixed with methane in the presence of a palladium catalyst, an explosive reaction takes place.

$$N_2O(g) \quad + \quad 2\,CH_4(g) \quad \rightarrow \quad N_2(g) \quad + \quad 2\,CO_2(g) \quad + \quad 4\,H_2O(g)$$

(*a*) Balance the above equation.

1

(*b*) Why can the palladium metal be described as a heterogeneous catalyst?

_____

_____

1

(*c*) The diagrams below show a possible model for palladium metal catalysing the reaction between dinitrogen oxide and methane.

Stage 1

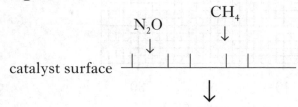

Statement

Reactants are adsorbed on to the catalyst surface.

Stage 2

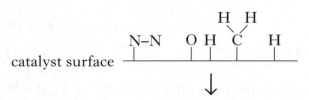

Bonds break.

Stage 3

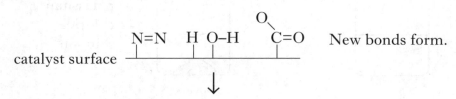

New bonds form.

Stage 4

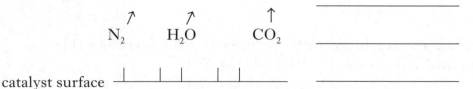

Add a statement describing what happens at **Stage 4**.

1

Marks

3. **(continued)**

(*d*) The presence of sulphur in methane gas can prevent the reaction from taking place.

Why would the presence of sulphur prevent the catalyst from working?

_____

_____

_____

_____ 1

(4)

[Turn over

DO N
WRIT
THI
MARC

Marks

4. In a **PPA**, a solution of copper (II) chloride was electrolysed.

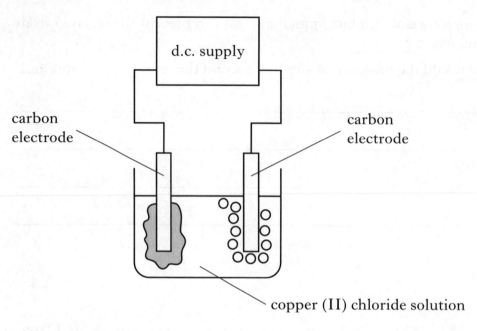

(a) What is meant by electrolysis?

_____

_____   1

(b) Why is it necessary to use a d.c. supply in electrolysis?

_____

_____   1

(c)   (i)   Complete the table by adding the charge for each electrode.

Observation at _____ electrode	Observation at _____ electrode
bubbles of gas	brown solid formed

1

(ii) How could the gas be identified?

_____

_____   1

(4)

Marks

5. Chlorofluorocarbons (CFCs) are a family of compounds which are highly effective as refrigerants and aerosol propellants. However, they are now known to damage the ozone layer.

One example of a CFC molecule is shown.

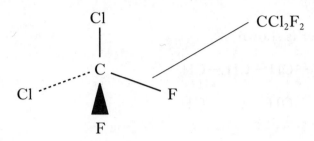

(*a*) What term is used to describe the **shape** of this molecule?

_____   1

(*b*) Scientists have developed compounds to replace CFCs. The table shows information about the ratio of atoms in CCl_2F_2 and compounds used to replace it.

Compound	Number of atoms				Atmospheric life (years)
	C	Cl	F	H	
CCl_2F_2	1	2	2	0	102
Replacement 1	1	1	2	1	13·3
Replacement 2	2	0	4	2	14·6
Replacement 3	1	0	2	2	5·6

(i) Draw a possible structure for Replacement 2.

1

(ii) Compared with CCl_2F_2, the replacement compounds contain less of which element?

_____   1

(iii) From the table, what is the advantage of using the replacement molecules as refrigerants and aerosol propellants?

_____   1

(4)

DO N
WRIT
TH
MAR(

Marks

6. Poly(ethenol) is one of the substances used to cover dishwasher tablets.

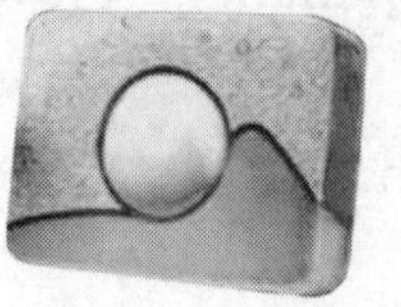

A section of the poly(ethenol) polymer is shown.

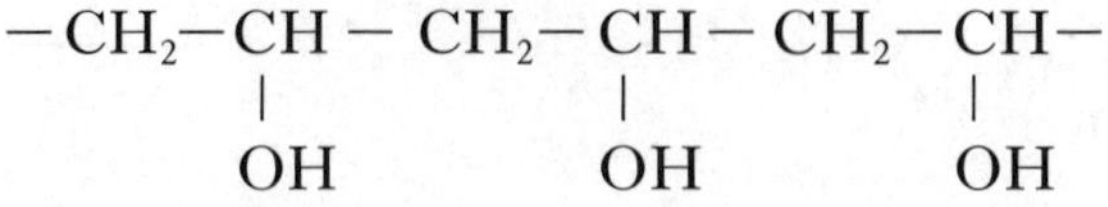

$$-CH_2-CH-CH_2-CH-CH_2-CH-$$
$$\qquad\quad |\qquad\qquad |\qquad\qquad |$$
$$\qquad\quad OH\qquad\quad OH\qquad\quad OH$$

(a) Name the functional group present in this polymer.

_____   **1**

(b) Draw the structure of the repeating unit for this polymer.

1

(c) A dishwasher tablet, complete with its poly(ethenol) cover, can be added to a dishwasher.

What property of the poly(ethenol) makes it suitable as a cover for a dishwasher tablet?

_____

_____   **1**

(3)

Marks

7. Scientists have replaced oils in gloss paints with synthetic polyesters. This has improved the drying quality of the paint.

   The first step in the production of the synthetic polyester is shown.

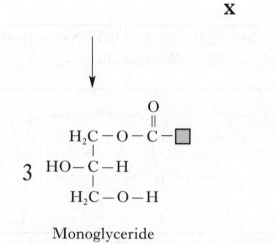

   Triglyceride   **X**

   Monoglyceride

   (a) What does the term synthetic mean?

   _____   1

   (b) Circle an ester link in the triglyceride.   1

   (c) Name **X**.

   _____   1

                                                       (3)

                                              [Turn over

DO N&
WRITE
THI
MAR&

Marks

8. Infrared spectroscopy can be used to detect the bonds present in molecules.
    The same bond always absorbs infrared radiation at the same wavenumber,
    even in different molecules.

    For example, the C–H bond absorbs in the range 2800 – 3000 wavenumbers.

    The infrared spectra of two different organic compounds are shown.

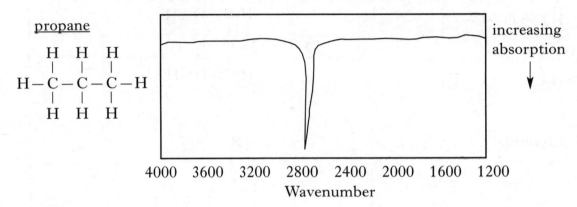

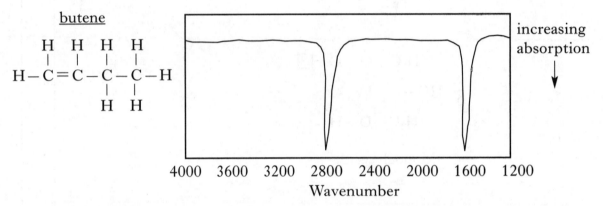

(a) The absorption at wavenumber 1600 in the spectrum of butene is not
     present in the spectrum of propane.

     Which bond could be responsible for this absorption?

     _____   1

(b) The O–H bond absorbs in the range 3500 – 3700 wavenumbers.

     Sketch the infrared spectrum you would predict for ethanol.

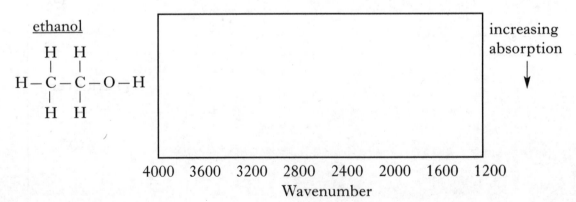

1

(2)

9. The enzyme phosphorylase catalyses the formation of starch from sugars.

Marks

(a) Name the monomer used to make a starch polymer.

_____

1

(b) Name the solution used to test for starch.

_____

1

(c) A student investigated the effect of temperature on the rate of starch formation. The results are shown.

Temperature (°C)	Relative rate $1/t$ (s^{-1})
4	0·003
12	0·010
16	0·016
20	0·022
24	0·033

(i) Plot these results as a line graph.
(Additional graph paper, if required, can be found on page 24.)

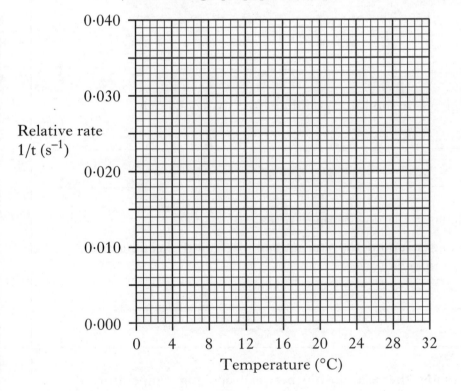

1

(ii) At 32 °C the relative rate was $0·0125s^{-1}$.
Use this rate to calculate the reaction time at 32 °C.

_____ seconds   1

(4)

Marks

10. **The Acid Test**
Adapted from Robert I. Wolke
November 2004

Seviche, a seafood dish, is described as "cooked" by marinating it in lime juice. Is it really "cooked" or is it still raw?

The citric acid in lime juice changes the proteins in fish. The normally twisted and folded protein molecules become unravelled and so the texture and colour of the fish change. This is known as denaturing.

Cooking also denatures proteins. The bonds that keep the protein twisted and folded are broken by heating the protein.

There are other methods which can be used to change the shape of proteins. Each method is complementary. For example, the stronger the acid that a protein is subjected to, the shorter the cooking time; the higher the temperature the shorter the cooking time.

Fish can therefore be cooked without heating it!

Use the article to answer the following questions.

(*a*) Proteins can be denatured.

Describe what happens to the protein when it is denatured.

_____

_____   1

(*b*) Other than heat, give a method that could be used to "cook" fish.

_____

_____   1

(*c*) Proteins can be denatured at low temperatures.

What does this suggest about the strength of the bonds keeping the protein twisted and folded?

_____

_____   1

(*d*) Draw a graph to show the relationship between cooking temperature and the cooking time for fish.

Cooking
temperature
(°C)

Cooking time

1

(4)

Marks

11. Silver jewellery slowly tarnishes in air. This is due to the formation of silver(I) sulphide.

The silver(I) sulphide can be converted back to silver using the following apparatus.

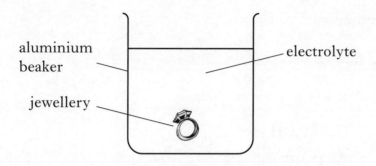

The equation for the reaction which takes place in the beaker is shown.

$$3Ag_2S(aq) \quad + \quad 2Al(s) \longrightarrow 6Ag(s) \quad + \quad Al_2S_3(aq)$$

(*a*) Calculate the mass of silver produced when 0·135 g of aluminium is used up.

_____ g   **2**

(*b*) How would you show that aluminium has been lost from the beaker during this reaction?

_____   **1**

(3)

[Turn over

Marks

12. Many medicines are available as tablets which dissolve readily in water. These tablets contain solid citric acid and sodium hydrogencarbonate.

(a) When the tablet is added to water the citric acid reacts with the sodium hydrogencarbonate giving off a gas.

Name the gas produced.

_____

1

(b) The structure of citric acid is shown below.

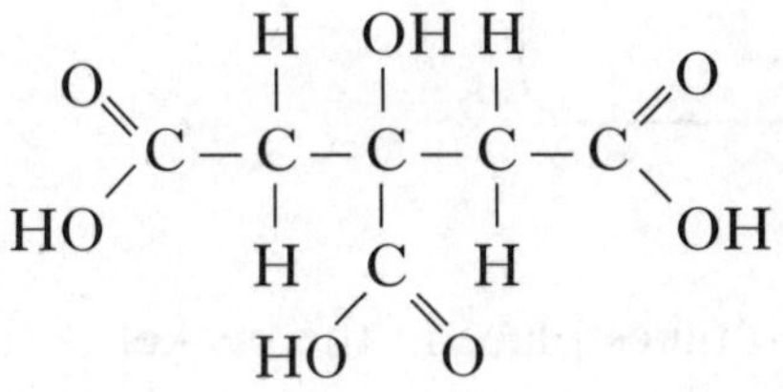

Write the molecular formula for citric acid.

_____

1

(c) In aqueous solution, citric acid molecules are only partially dissociated. What term is used to describe this type of acid?

_____

1

(3)

Marks

13. Strontium nitrate is used in fireworks. The flow chart shows how strontium nitrate can be produced.

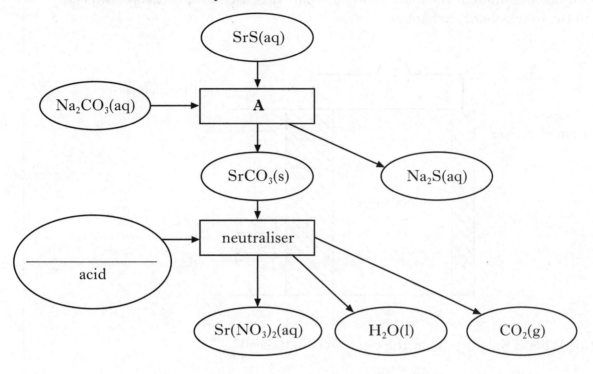

   (a) Name the type of chemical reaction taking place at **A**.

   _____ 1

   (b) Complete the flow chart by adding the name of the acid used to form the salt, strontium nitrate.

   _____ 1

   (c) What colour would be seen when a firework containing strontium nitrate is set off?

   (You may wish to use page 4 of the data booklet to help you.)

   _____ 1

                                                (3)

[Turn over

Marks

14. A number of electrochemical cells are being developed.

One such example is the aluminium/air cell. It is used as a back-up power supply in telephone exchanges.

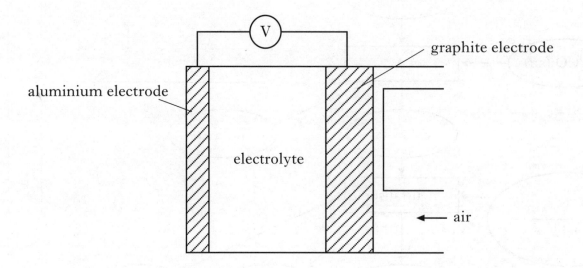

(*a*) What is the purpose of the electrolyte in the cell?

_____

_____   1

(*b*) The ion-electron equations for the reactions taking place at the electrodes are:

aluminium electrode	$Al \rightarrow Al^{3+} + 3e^-$
graphite electrode	$O_2 + 2H_2O + 4e^- \rightarrow 4OH^-$

(i) What process has the aluminium electrode undergone?

_____   1

(ii) When the cell is operating, a solid forms in the electrolyte.

Identify the solid.

(You may wish to use page 5 of the data booklet to help you.)

_____   1

(3)

Marks

15. A student's report is shown for the **PPA "Reactions of Metals with Oxygen"**.

Title.	Reactions of Metals with Oxygen. **Date.** 15/11/07
Aim.	The aim of the experiment was to place zinc, copper and magnesium in order of reactivity.
Procedure.	The apparatus required to carry out the experiment was collected and assembled as shown.

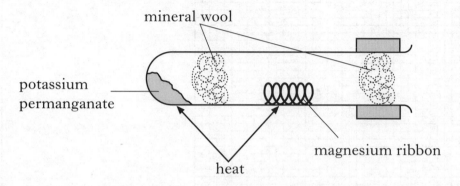

Results

Metal	Observations
zinc	moderately fast reaction
magnesium	fast reaction
copper	slow reaction

(a) Write the formula for potassium permanganate.

(You may wish to use page 4 of the data booklet to help you.)

_____

1

(b) Why is potassium permanganate used in the experiment?

_____

_____

1

(c) For safety reasons it is recommended that metal powders should not be used when carrying out this experiment.

Suggest why metal powders should **not** be used.

_____

_____

_____

1

(3)

[END OF QUESTION PAPER]

ADDITIONAL SPACE FOR ANSWERS

ADDITIONAL GRAPH PAPER FOR QUESTION 9(c)(i)

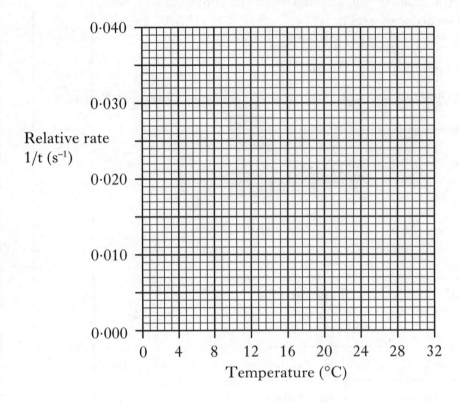

ADDITIONAL SPACE FOR ANSWERS

ADDITIONAL SPACE FOR ANSWERS

ADDITIONAL SPACE FOR ANSWERS

[BLANK PAGE]

INTERMEDIATE 2

2009

[BLANK PAGE]

FOR OFFICIAL USE

Section B   Total Marks

X012/201

NATIONAL
QUALIFICATIONS
2009

WEDNESDAY, 3 JUNE
9.00 AM – 11.00 AM

CHEMISTRY
INTERMEDIATE 2

Fill in these boxes and read what is printed below.

Full name of centre

Town

Forename(s)

Surname

Date of birth
Day Month Year   Scottish candidate number   Number of seat

Necessary data will be found in the Chemistry Data Booklet for Standard Grade and Intermediate 2.

Section A – Questions 1–30 (30 marks)

Instructions for completion of **Section A** are given on page two.

For this section of the examination you must use an **HB pencil**.

Section B (50 marks)

All questions should be attempted.

The questions may be answered in any order but all answers are to be written in the spaces provided in this answer book, **and must be written clearly and legibly in ink**.

Rough work, if any should be necessary, should be written in this book, and then scored through when the fair copy has been written. If further space is required, a supplementary sheet for rough work may be obtained from the invigilator.

Additional space for answers will be found at the end of the book. If further space is required, supplementary sheets may be obtained from the invigilator and should be inserted inside the **front** cover of this booklet.

Before leaving the examination room you must give this book to the invigilator. If you do not, you may lose all the marks for this paper.

Read carefully

1 Check that the answer sheet provided is for **Chemistry Intermediate 2 (Section A)**.

2 For this section of the examination you must use an **HB pencil** and, where necessary, an eraser.

3 Check that the answer sheet you have been given has **your name**, **date of birth**, **SCN** (Scottish Candidate Number) and **Centre Name** printed on it.

   Do not change any of these details.

4 If any of this information is wrong, tell the Invigilator immediately.

5 If this information is correct, **print** your name and seat number in the boxes provided.

6 The answer to each question is **either** A, B, C or D. Decide what your answer is, then, using your pencil, put a horizontal line in the space provided (see sample question below).

7 There is **only one correct** answer to each question.

8 Any rough working should be done on the question paper or the rough working sheet, **not** on your answer sheet.

9 At the end of the exam, put the **answer sheet for Section A inside the front cover of this answer book**.

Sample Question

To show that the ink in a ball-pen consists of a mixture of dyes, the method of separation would be

      A   chromatography

      B   fractional distillation

      C   fractional crystallisation

      D   filtration.

The correct answer is **A**—chromatography. The answer **A** has been clearly marked in **pencil** with a horizontal line (see below).

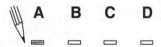

Changing an answer

If you decide to change your answer, carefully erase your first answer and using your pencil, fill in the answer you want. The answer below has been changed to **D**.

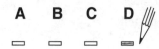

SECTION A

1. Which of the following gases is a noble gas?

A   Argon

B   Oxygen

C   Fluorine

D   Nitrogen

2. Which line in the table correctly shows how the concentration of a solution changes by adding more solute or by adding more solvent?

	Adding solute	Adding solvent
A	concentration falls	concentration rises
B	concentration falls	concentration falls
C	concentration rises	concentration falls
D	concentration rises	concentration rises

3. Magnesium and zinc both react with hydrochloric acid.

In which of the following experiments would the reaction rate be fastest?

A
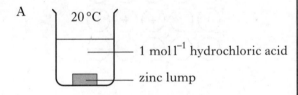
20 °C
1 mol l^{-1} hydrochloric acid
zinc lump

B
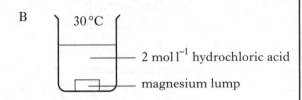
30 °C
2 mol l^{-1} hydrochloric acid
magnesium lump

C
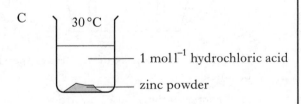
30 °C
1 mol l^{-1} hydrochloric acid
zinc powder

D
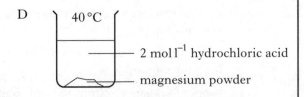
40 °C
2 mol l^{-1} hydrochloric acid
magnesium powder

4. The table shows the numbers of protons, electrons and neutrons in four particles, **W**, **X**, **Y** and **Z**.

Particle	Protons	Electrons	Neutrons
W	17	17	18
X	11	11	12
Y	17	17	20
Z	18	18	18

Which pair of particles are isotopes?

A   **W** and **X**

B   **W** and **Y**

C   **X** and **Y**

D   **Y** and **Z**

5. When solid sodium chloride dissolves in water, a solution containing sodium ions and chloride ions is formed.

Which of the following equations correctly shows the state symbols for this process?

A $NaCl(s) + H_2O(\ell) \rightarrow Na^+(\ell) + Cl^-(\ell)$

B $NaCl(s) + H_2O(\ell) \rightarrow Na^+(aq) + Cl^-(aq)$

C $NaCl(s) + H_2O(aq) \rightarrow Na^+(aq) + Cl^-(aq)$

D $NaCl(aq) + H_2O(\ell) \rightarrow Na^+(aq) + Cl^-(aq)$

6. Metallic bonding is a force of attraction between

A   positive ions and delocalised electrons

B   negative ions and delocalised electrons

C   negative ions and positive ions

D   a shared pair of electrons and two nuclei.

[Turn over

7. The table gives information about the attraction some atoms have for bonded electrons.

Atom	Attraction for electrons
C I Br Cl F	least ↓ greatest

Which of the following bonds is the **least** polar?

A   C – F

B   C – Cl

C   C – Br

D   C – I

8. Which of the following diagrams represents a **compound** made up of **diatomic** molecules?

A

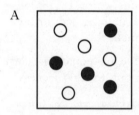

B

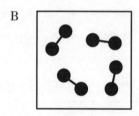

C

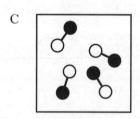

D

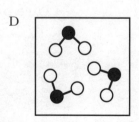

9. Which of the following diagrams could be used to represent the structure of sodium chloride?

A

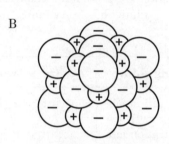

B

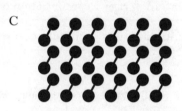

C

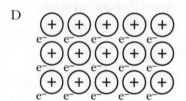

D

10.

During the electrolysis of molten copper(II) bromide

A   copper atoms lose electrons to form copper ions

B   bromine molecules gain electrons to form bromide ions

C   bromide ions gain electrons to form bromine molecules

D   copper ions gain electrons to form copper atoms.

11. What is the name of the compound with the formula Ag_2O?

    A   Silver(I) oxide

    B   Silver(II) oxide

    C   Silver(III) oxide

    D   Silver(IV) oxide

12. Which of the following exhaust emissions is most likely to come from the incomplete combustion of diesel?

    A   Water vapour

    B   Soot particles

    C   Carbon dioxide

    D   Nitrogen dioxide

13. The apparatus shown can be used to identify what is produced when a gas is burned.

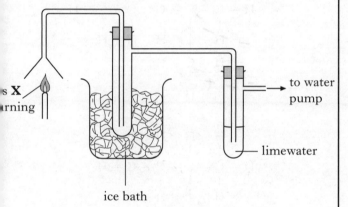

    When gas **X** was burned, a colourless liquid collected in the cooled test tube but there was no change in the limewater.

    Gas **X** could be

    A   methane

    B   carbon monoxide

    C   hydrogen

    D   ethene.

14. The fractional distillation of crude oil produces a number of different fractions.

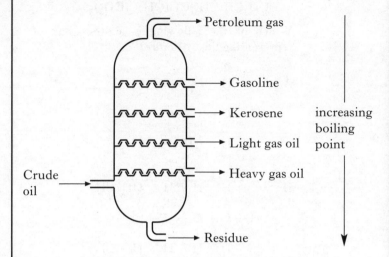

    Compared with the heavy gas oil fraction, the kerosene fraction

    A   is less flammable and contains larger hydrocarbon molecules

    B   is less flammable and contains smaller hydrocarbon molecules

    C   is more flammable and contains larger hydrocarbon molecules

    D   is more flammable and contains smaller hydrocarbon molecules.

15. Which of the following could be the molecular formula of a cycloalkane?

    A C_7H_{10}

    B C_7H_{12}

    C C_7H_{14}

    D C_7H_{16}

[Turn over

16. The shortened structural formula for an organic compound is

$$CH_3CH(CH_3)CH(OH)C(CH_3)_3.$$

Which of the following is another way of representing this structure?

A
```
    H   H   OH  CH₃
    |   |   |   |
H — C — C — C — C — CH₃
    |   |   |   |
    H   CH₃ H   CH₃
```

B
```
    H   H   H   OH  CH₃
    |   |   |   |   |
H — C — C — C — C — C — CH₃
    |   |   |   |   |
    H   H   H   H   CH₃
```

C
```
    H   H   H   CH₃ CH₃
    |   |   |   |   |
H — C — C — C — C — C — H
    |   |   |   |   |
    H   CH₃ OH  H   H
```

D
```
    H   H   H   H   H   H
    |   |   |   |   |   |
H — C — C — C — C — C — C — CH₃
    |   |   |   |   |   |
    H   CH₃ OH  H   H   H
```

17.
```
    H   OH  H   H
    |   |   |   |
H — C — C — C — C — H
    |   |   |   |
    H   |   H   H
    H — C — H
        |
        H
```

The above compound could be formed by adding water to

A
```
    H   H
    |   |
H — C — C — C = C — H
    |   |   |   |
    H   |   H   H
    H — C — H
        |
        H
```

B
```
    H                   H
    |                   |
H — C — C — C = C — C — H
    |   |   |   |   |
    H   |   H   H   H
    H — C — H
        |
        H
```

C
```
    H   H   H   H
    |   |   |   |
H — C — C — C — C — H
    |   |   |   |
    H   |   H   H
    H — C — H
        |
        H
```

D
```
            H   H
            |   |
H — C = C — C — C — H
    |   |   |   |
    H   |   H   H
    H — C — H
        |
        H
```

18. Part of the structure of an addition polymer is shown below. It is made using two different monomers.

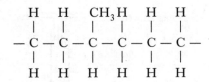

Which pair of alkenes could be used as monomers for this polymer?

A   Ethene and propene

B   Ethene and butene

C   Propene and butene

D   Ethene and pentene

19. In which of the following experiments would **both** carbohydrates give an orange precipitate when heated with Benedict's solution?

A

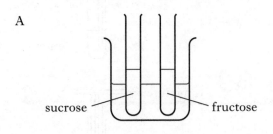

sucrose   fructose

B

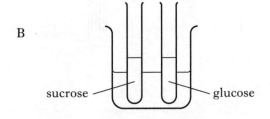

sucrose   glucose

C

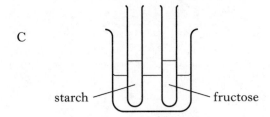

starch   fructose

D

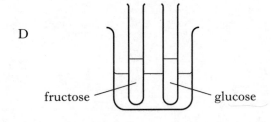

fructose   glucose

20. Glycerol can be obtained from a fat by

A   hydrolysis

B   esterification

C   condensation

D   neutralisation.

21. Which oxide, when shaken with water, would leave the pH unchanged?

(You may wish to use page 5 of the data booklet to help you.)

A   Calcium oxide

B   Carbon dioxide

C   Sulphur dioxide

D   Zinc oxide

22. Two tests were carried out on compound **X**.

Test 1

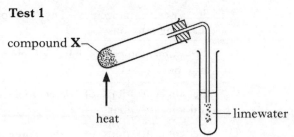

compound **X**   limewater

heat

Test 2   compound **X**

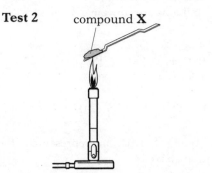

The following results were obtained.

Test	Result
1	limewater turns cloudy
2	flame turns blue-green

Which of the following could be compound **X**?

(You may wish to use page 4 of the data booklet to help you.)

A   Barium carbonate

B   Copper carbonate

C   Copper sulphate

D   Sodium sulphate

23. Which line in the table correctly shows the properties of $0 \cdot 1$ mol l^{-1} ethanoic acid compared to $0 \cdot 1$ mol l^{-1} hydrochloric acid?

	pH	Conductivity	Rate of reaction with magnesium
A	higher	lower	slower
B	lower	higher	faster
C	higher	higher	faster
D	lower	lower	slower

24. In water, an equilibrium exists between water molecules and hydrogen and hydroxide ions.

$$H_2O(\ell) \rightleftharpoons H^+(aq) + OH^-(aq)$$

At equilibrium

A   the water molecules have stopped changing into ions

B   the water molecules have all changed into ions

C   the concentrations of water molecules and ions are equal

D   the concentrations of water molecules and ions are constant.

25. $2K^+(aq) + 2I^-(aq) + Pb^{2+}(aq) + 2NO_3^-(aq)$

↓

$Pb^{2+}(I^-)_2(s) + 2K^+(aq) + 2NO_3^-(aq)$

The type of reaction represented by the equation above is

A   addition

B   neutralisation

C   precipitation

D   redox.

26. Which of the following diagrams shows the apparatus which would allow a soluble gas to be removed from a mixture of gases?

A

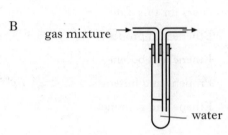

B

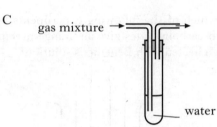

C

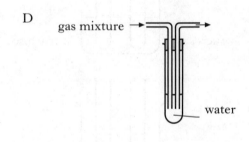

D

27. Which pair of metals, when connected in a cell, would give the highest voltage and a flow of electrons from **X** to **Y**?

(You may wish to use page 7 of the data booklet to help you.)

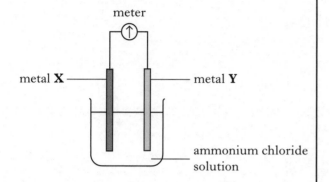

meter

metal **X** ——— ——— metal **Y**

ammonium chloride solution

	Metal X	Metal Y
A	magnesium	copper
B	copper	magnesium
C	zinc	tin
D	tin	zinc

28. The ion-electron equation

$$Ti(s) \rightarrow Ti^{2+}(aq) + 2e^-$$

represents the

A reduction of titanium atoms

B reduction of titanium ions

C oxidation of titanium atoms

D oxidation of titanium ions.

29. The following statements relate to four different metals, **P**, **Q**, **R** and **S**.

Metal **P** displaces metal **Q** from a solution containing ions of **Q**.

In a cell, electrons flow from metal **S** to metal **P**.

Metal **R** is the only metal which can be obtained from its ore by heat alone.

The order of reactivity of the metals, starting with the **most** reactive is

A **S, P, Q, R**

B **R, Q, P, S**

C **R, S, Q, P**

D **S, Q, P, R**.

30.

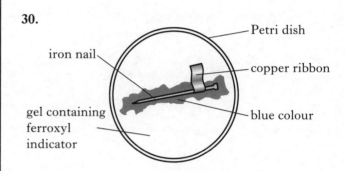

Petri dish

iron nail

copper ribbon

gel containing ferroxyl indicator

blue colour

Which ion gives a blue colour with ferroxyl indicator?

A $OH^-(aq)$

B $Fe^{2+}(aq)$

C $Fe^{3+}(aq)$

D $Cu^{2+}(aq)$

Candidates are reminded that the answer sheet for Section A MUST be placed INSIDE the front cover of this answer book.

[Turn over

[BLANK PAGE]

Marks

SECTION B

50 marks are available in this section of the paper.

All answers must be written clearly and legibly in ink.

1. Atoms contain particles called protons, neutrons and electrons.

   The nuclide notation of the sodium atom is shown.

   $$^{24}_{11}Na$$

   (*a*) Complete the table to show the number of each type of particle in this sodium atom.

Particle	Number
electron	11
proton	
neutron	

   1

   (*b*) Electrons are arranged in energy levels.

   (i) Complete the diagram to show how the electrons are arranged in a sodium atom.

   (You may wish to use page 1 of the data booklet to help you.)

   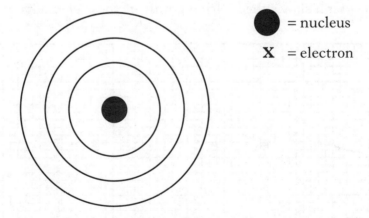

   = nucleus

   X = electron

   1

   (ii) Explain what holds the negatively charged electrons in place around the nucleus.

   _____

   _____

   1

   (3)

Marks

2. The diagram shows the apparatus used to prepare chlorine gas. Concentrated hydrochloric acid is reacted with potassium permanganate. The gas produced is bubbled through water to remove any unreacted hydrochloric acid and is then dried by bubbling through concentrated sulphuric acid.

(*a*) Complete the diagram for the preparation of chlorine gas by adding the labels for concentrated sulphuric acid, potassium permanganate and water.

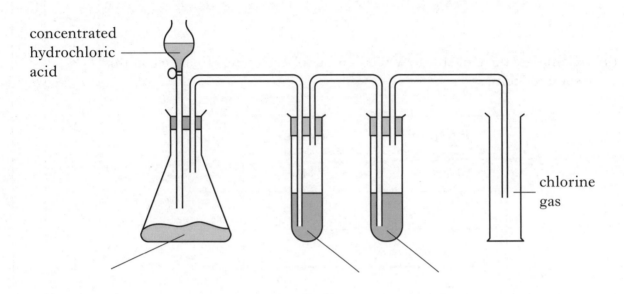

1

(*b*) Chlorine is a member of the Group 7 elements.

The graph shows the melting points of these elements.

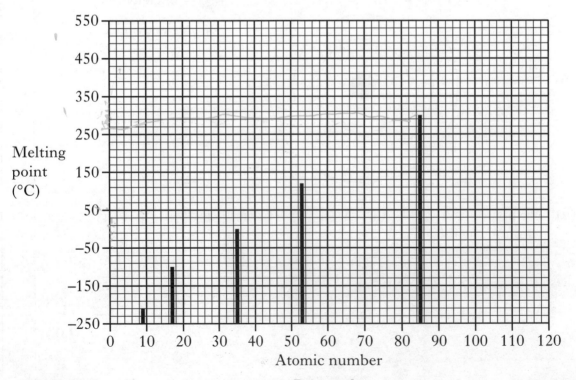

Page twelve

DO NOT WRITE IN THIS MARGIN

Marks

2. (*b*) (continued)

(i) State the relationship between the atomic number and the melting point of the Group 7 elements.

____

____

____ **1**

(ii) The next member of this group would have an atomic number of 117.

Using the graph, predict the melting point of this element.

Melting point ______________ °C **1**

(3)

[Turn over

Marks

3. When calcium chloride is dissolved in water, heat is released to the surroundings.

(*a*) What term is used to describe chemical reactions which give out heat?

_____   1

(*b*) A student investigated how changing the mass of calcium chloride affects the heat released.

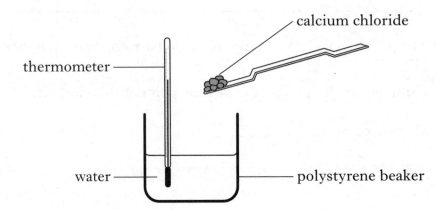

The results are shown.

Mass of calcium chloride used (g)	Highest temperature reached (°C)
0	20
5	28
10	34
15	41
20	50
25	57

Marks

3. **(b)** **(continued)**

(i) Plot a line graph of these results.

(Additional graph paper, if required, can be found on page 30.)

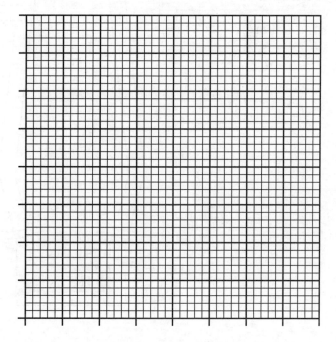

2

(ii) Using your graph, find the mass of calcium chloride that would give a temperature of 40 °C.

_____ g

1

(c) State an advantage of using a polystyrene beaker in this experiment.

_____

_____

1

(5)

[Turn over

Marks

4. Iron is produced from iron ore in a Blast Furnace.

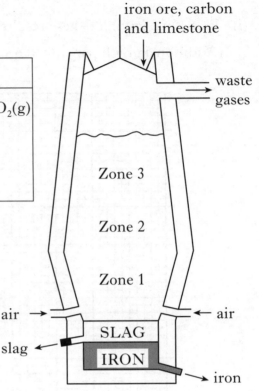

Zone	Key reaction
3	$Fe_2O_3(s) + CO(g) \rightarrow Fe(\ell) + CO_2(g)$
2	$CO_2(g) + C(s) \rightarrow 2CO(g)$
1	$C(s) + O_2(g) \rightarrow CO_2(g)$

(a) The key reaction which takes place in Zone 3 is shown.

$$Fe_2O_3(s) + CO(g) \rightarrow Fe(\ell) + CO_2(g)$$

Balance this equation.   1

(b) The equation for the key reaction in Zone 2 is shown below. Calculate the mass of carbon monoxide produced when 1200 kg of carbon reacts.

$$CO_2(g) + C(s) \rightarrow 2CO(g)$$

_____ kg   **2**

(c) Why is air blown into the Blast Furnace?

_____   1

(4)

Marks

5. Air is a mixture of gases. These gases can be separated by the process of fractional distillation.

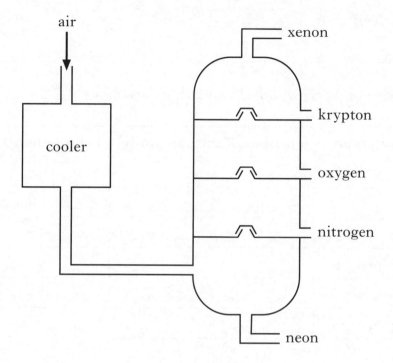

(*a*) Why can these gases be separated by fractional distillation?

_____

_____   1

(*b*) Nitrogen is separated from the mixture at −200 °C.

Circle the state that nitrogen will be in at this temperature.

(You may wish to use page 3 of your data booklet to help you.)

solid   liquid   gas   1

(*c*) The cooler contains sodium hydroxide solution. This reacts with the carbon dioxide in the air and removes it from the mixture of gases.

Name the type of chemical reaction taking place.

_____   1

(3)

[Turn over

Marks

6. The octane number of petrol is a measure of how efficiently it burns as a fuel. The higher the octane number, the more efficient the fuel.

(*a*) What is a fuel?

_____   1

(*b*) The octane numbers for some hydrocarbons are shown.

Hydrocarbon	Number of carbon atoms	Octane number
hexane	6	
heptane	7	0
octane	8	−19
2-methylpentane	6	71
2-methylhexane	7	44
2-methylheptane	8	23

(i) Predict the octane number for hexane.

_____   1

(ii) State a relationship between the structure of the hydrocarbon and their efficiency as fuels.

_____

_____

_____   1

(3)

Marks

7. The diagram shows how paraffin, $C_{12}H_{26}$, can be cracked.

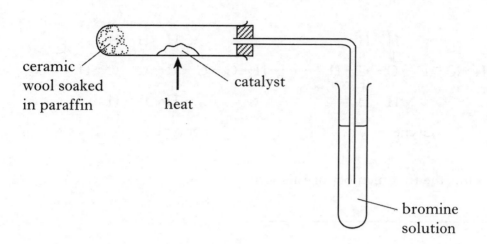

ceramic
wool soaked
in paraffin   heat   catalyst

bromine
solution

(a) Name the catalyst used in cracking.

_____   **1**

(b) One of the reactions taking place when paraffin is cracked is

$$C_{12}H_{26} \longrightarrow C_8H_{18} + \mathbf{X}$$

(i) Identify molecule **X**.

_____   **1**

(ii) Describe what would be **seen** when **X** is added to bromine
solution.

_____

_____   **1**

                                                        (3)

[Turn over

Marks

8. Alkynes are a homologous series of hydrocarbons which contain carbon to carbon triple bonds. Two members of this series are shown.

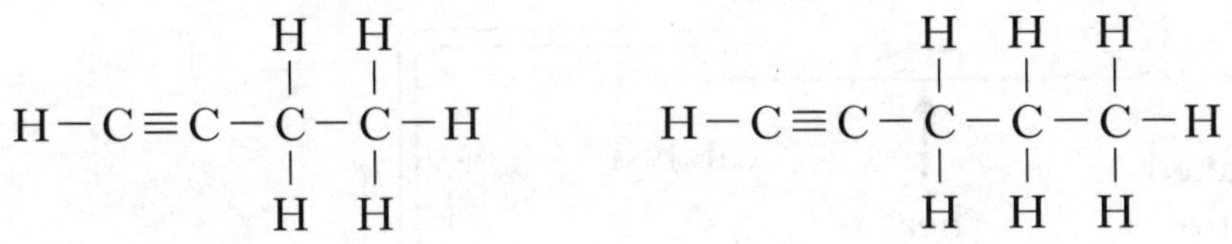

$$H-C\equiv C-\underset{\underset{H}{|}}{\overset{\overset{H}{|}}{C}}-\underset{\underset{H}{|}}{\overset{\overset{H}{|}}{C}}-H$$

butyne

$$H-C\equiv C-\underset{\underset{H}{|}}{\overset{\overset{H}{|}}{C}}-\underset{\underset{H}{|}}{\overset{\overset{H}{|}}{C}}-\underset{\underset{H}{|}}{\overset{\overset{H}{|}}{C}}-H$$

pentyne

(a) Name the first member of this series.

_____   1

(b) Alkynes can be prepared by reacting a dibromoalkane with potassium hydroxide solution.

$$H-\underset{\underset{Br}{|}}{\overset{\overset{H}{|}}{C}}-\underset{\underset{Br}{|}}{\overset{\overset{H}{|}}{C}}-\underset{\underset{H}{|}}{\overset{\overset{H}{|}}{C}}-H \ + \ 2KOH \ \rightarrow \ H-C\equiv C-\underset{\underset{H}{|}}{\overset{\overset{H}{|}}{C}}-H \ + \ 2KBr \ + \ H_2O$$

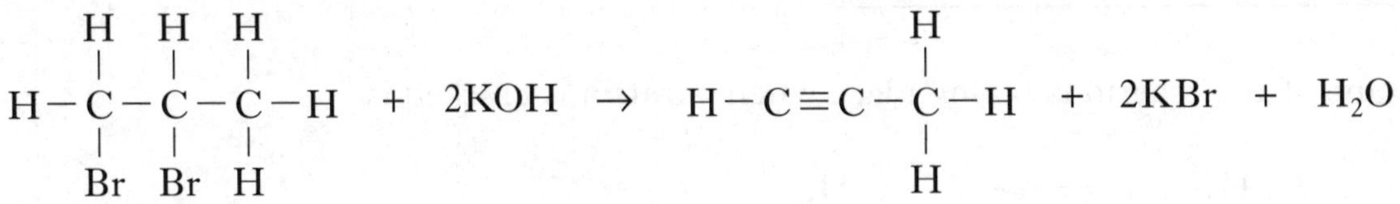

dibromoalkane   propyne

(i) Draw a structural formula for the alkyne formed when the dibromoalkane shown reacts with potassium hydroxide solution.

$$H-\underset{\underset{H}{|}}{\overset{\overset{H}{|}}{C}}-\underset{\underset{Br}{|}}{\overset{\overset{H}{|}}{C}}-\underset{\underset{Br}{|}}{\overset{\overset{H}{|}}{C}}-\underset{\underset{H}{|}}{\overset{\overset{H}{|}}{C}}-H \ + \ 2KOH \ \rightarrow$$

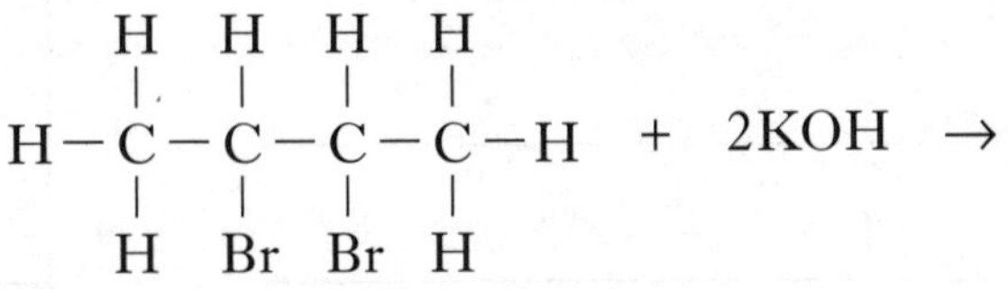

1

(ii) Suggest a reason why the dibromoalkane shown below does not form an alkyne when it is added to potassium hydroxide solution.

$$H-\underset{\underset{H}{|}}{\overset{\overset{H}{|}}{C}}-\underset{\underset{Br}{|}}{\overset{\overset{H}{|}}{C}}-\underset{\underset{H}{|}}{\overset{\overset{H}{|}}{C}}-\underset{\underset{Br}{|}}{\overset{\overset{H}{|}}{C}}-\underset{\underset{H}{|}}{\overset{\overset{H}{|}}{C}}-H$$

_____

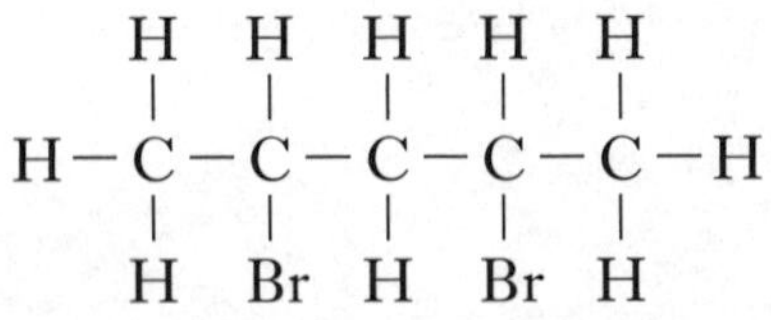

_____   1

(3)

Marks

9. The enzyme RuBisCo is one of the most abundant enzymes on Earth. It contains lysine at its active site.

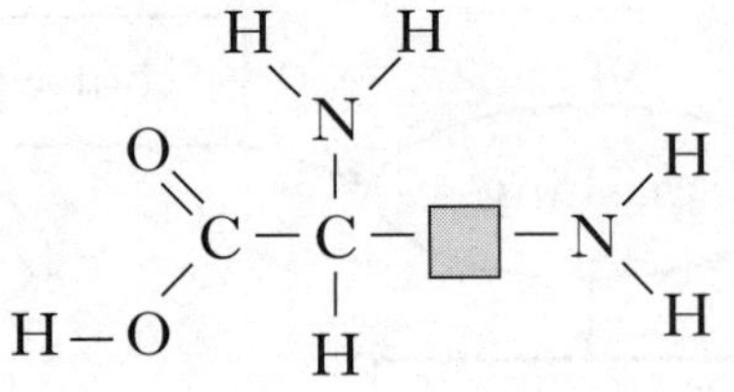

lysine

(a) Lysine contains two different types of functional groups.

Circle an amine group in the lysine molecule shown above.   **1**

(b) Name the family of compounds to which lysine belongs.

_____   **1**

(c) Complete the equation to show the structure of the other product formed when two molecules of lysine react.

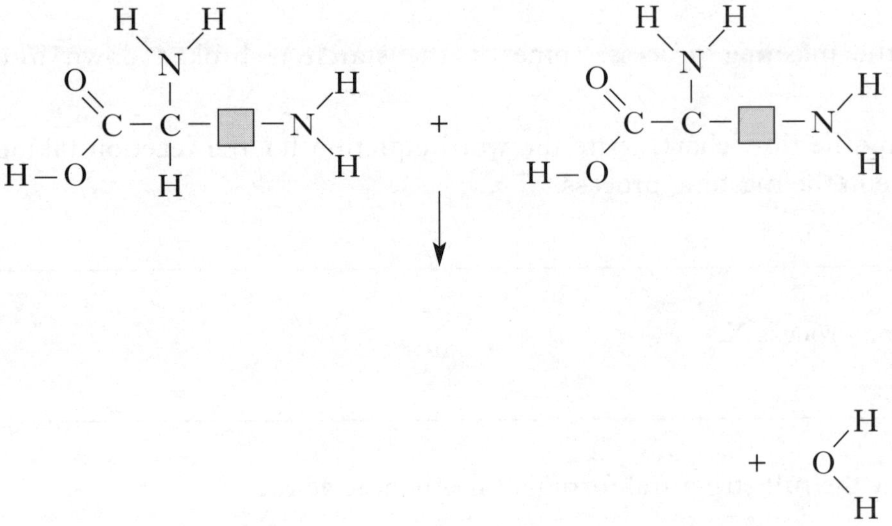

1

(3)

[Turn over

DO NO
WRITE
THIS
MARGI

Marks

10. The flow chart shows some of the stages in the manufacture of ethanoic acid.

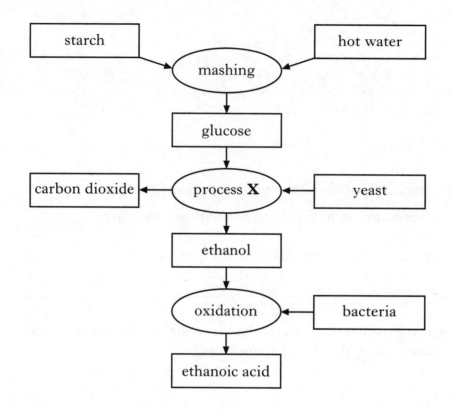

(a) In the mashing process, some of the starch is broken down into glucose.

Using the flow chart, write the word equation for the reaction taking place in the mashing process.

_____   1

(b) Name process **X**.

_____   1

(c) Draw the full structural formula for ethanoic acid.

1

(d) Ethanoic acid can be reacted with methanol to form an ester, which is used as a solvent in nail varnish remover.

Name this ester.

_____   1

(4)

DO NOT
WRITE IN
THIS
MARGIN

Marks

11. Urea is a substance found in human urine. The enzyme urease catalyses the hydrolysis of urea. During the reaction, ammonia and carbon dioxide are produced.

$$NH_2CONH_2(aq) + H_2O(\ell) \longrightarrow 2NH_3(aq) + CO_2(g)$$

(a) What is an enzyme?

_____   1

(b) The ammonia solution produced in this reaction is described as a weak base.

(i) What is meant by a weak base?

_____

_____   1

(ii) The concentration of ammonia solution can be determined as follows:

1   pipette $10\,cm^3$ of ammonia solution into a conical flask
2   add 3 drops of indicator solution
3   add $0{\cdot}1\,mol\,l^{-1}$ of hydrochloric acid from a burette until the indicator changes colour

Name this technique.

_____   1
(3)

[Turn over

Marks

12. Rhubarb contains oxalic acid, $C_2H_2O_4$. Oxalic acid decolourises acidified potassium permanganate solution.

An experiment was carried out to time how long it takes to decolourise the solution using different numbers of rhubarb cubes.

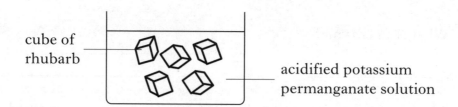

cube of rhubarb

acidified potassium permanganate solution

The results are shown.

Number of rhubarb cubes	Time to decolourise solution(s)	Relative rate (1/t) (s^{-1})
5	360	0·003
10		0·006
15	92	0·011
20	40	0·025

(a) Calculate the time taken for 10 cubes of rhubarb to decolourise the solution.

_____ s   **1**

(b) Using collision theory, explain why increasing the number of rhubarb cubes increases the rate of reaction.

_____

_____   **1**

Marks

12.   **(continued)**

(c)   The equation for the reaction between permanganate solution and the oxalic acid in rhubarb is

$$2MnO_4^- + 5C_2H_2O_4 + 6H^+ \longrightarrow 2Mn^{2+} + 10CO_2 + 8H_2O.$$
2 moles   5 moles

(i)   Calculate the number of moles of permanganate ions (MnO_4^-) in $100 \, cm^3$ of a $1 \cdot 0 \, mol \, l^{-1}$ solution.

_____ mol   **1**

(ii)   The above equation shows that 2 moles of permanganate ions react with 5 moles of oxalic acid.

How many moles of oxalic acid ($C_2H_2O_4$) react with $100 \, cm^3$ of $1 \cdot 0 \, mol \, l^{-1}$ permanganate (MnO_4^-) solution?

_____ mol   **1**

(4)

[Turn over

Marks

13. Part of a student's PPA sheet is shown.

Intermediate 2 Chemistry	Preparation of a Salt	Unit 3 PPA1

Aim

The aim of this experiment is to make a magnesium salt by the reaction of magnesium/magnesium carbonate with sulphuric acid.

Procedure

1. Using a measuring cylinder add 20 cm³ of dilute acid to the beaker.

2. Add a spatulaful of magnesium or magnesium carbonate to the acid and stir the reaction mixture with a glass rod.

3. If all the solid reacts add another spatulaful of magnesium or magnesium carbonate and stir the mixture.

4. Continue adding the magnesium or magnesium carbonate until . . .

(a) Complete the instruction for step 4 of the procedure.

_____

_____

_____   **1**

(b) Why is an excess of magnesium or magnesium carbonate added to the acid?

_____

_____

_____   **1**

(c) The equation for the preparation of magnesium sulphate from magnesium carbonate is shown.

$$MgCO_3(s) + H_2SO_4(aq) \rightarrow MgSO_4(aq) + \rule{1cm}{0.4pt} + \rule{1cm}{0.4pt}$$

Complete the equation showing the formulae for the missing products.   **1**

Marks

14. When iron reacts with water and oxygen, rust forms.

The chemical name for rust is iron(III) oxide.

(*a*) Write the chemical formula for rust.

_____

1

(*b*) During rusting, iron initially loses 2 electrons to form iron(II) ions. These are further oxidised to form iron(III) ions.

Write the ion-electron equation to show iron(II) ions forming iron(III) ions.

(You may wish to use page 7 of the data booklet to help you.)

_____

1

(*c*) Some iron railings were fixed into stone walls by using plugs of lead. Over time, the iron railings rusted faster at the point of contact with the lead.

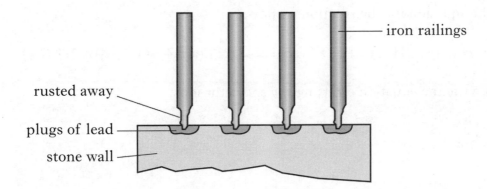

Why does lead increase the rate of rusting?

_____

_____

1

(3)

[Turn over

DO NO
WRITE
THIS
MARG

Marks

15. The reaction between sodium hydroxide solution and dilute sulphuric acid can be followed by measuring the conductivity of the reaction mixture.

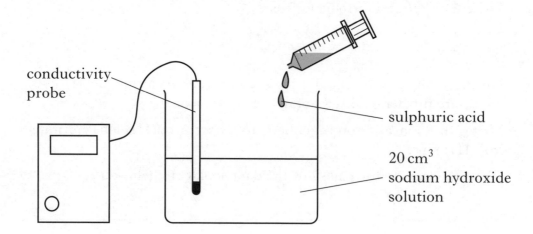

The conductivity probe measures the conductivity of the solution as the reaction proceeds.

(a) The equation for the reaction is shown.

$$2Na^+(aq) + 2OH^-(aq) + 2H^+(aq) + SO_4^{2-}(aq) \longrightarrow 2Na^+(aq) + SO_4^{2-}(aq) + 2H_2O(\ell)$$

Rewrite the equation omitting the spectator ions.

1

(b) The experiment was repeated using $20\,cm^3$ barium hydroxide solution.

The results of both experiments are shown in the table.

Solution	Conductivity at start (mA)	Conductivity at end-point (mA)
$0{\cdot}1\ mol\,l^{-1}\ NaOH(aq)$	80	35
$0{\cdot}1\ mol\,l^{-1}\ Ba(OH)_2(aq)$	160	0

(i) Why does barium hydroxide solution have a higher conductivity than the sodium hydroxide solution at the start?

_____

_____

1

Marks

15. **(b)** **(continued)**

The equation for the reaction between barium hydroxide solution and sulphuric acid is shown.

$$Ba^{2+}(aq) + 2OH^-(aq) + 2H^+(aq) + SO_4^{2-}(aq) \longrightarrow Ba^{2+}SO_4^{2-}(s) + 2H_2O(\ell)$$

(ii) Why is the conductivity reading at the end point 0 mA?

_____

_____

1

(3)

[END OF QUESTION PAPER]

DO NO
WRITE
THIS
MARG

ADDITIONAL SPACE FOR ANSWERS

ADDITIONAL GRAPH PAPER FOR QUESTION 3(*b*)(i)

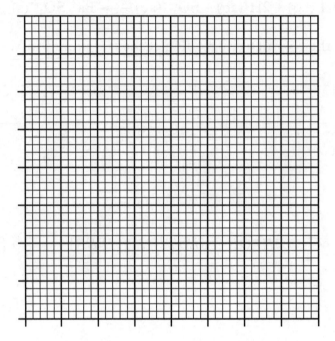

ADDITIONAL SPACE FOR ANSWERS

Acknowledgements

Permission has been sought from all relevant copyright holders and Bright Red Publishing is grateful for the use of the following:

Extract adapted from 'The Acid Test' by Robert I Wolke, taken from The Washington Post 10 November 2004 © Robert I Wolke (2008 page 18).

CHEMISTRY INTERMEDIATE 2

2006

SECTION A

1. D	2. A	3. C
4. C	5. B	6. A
7. D	8. C	9. B
10. A	11. B	12. D
13. A	14. B	15. B
16. C	17. B	18. C
19. A	20. C	21. D
22. C	23. A	24. A
25. D	26. A	27. C
28. B	29. D	30. D

SECTION B

1. (a) Acid rain

   (b) (i) $2CH_3SH + H_2 \longrightarrow C_2H_6 + 2H_2S$ *(or multiple)*

   (ii) 445°C

2. (a) A covalent bond is a pair of electrons shared by two atoms

   (b)

   (c) (i) Paper X - Blue; Paper Y - Red
   (ii) Ammonium chloride

3. (a) 2 negative (2−)

   (b) $Fe^{3+} + 3e^- \longrightarrow Fe$

   (c) Protons   26
   Neutrons 30
   Electrons 23

4. (a) The solution goes cloudy obscuring the cross
   A solid is formed/a precipitate is formed

   (b)

   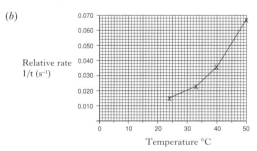

   (c) (i) $0\cdot050\,s^{-1}$

   (ii) 8 s

   (d) So depth of liquid and hence amount of sulphur needed to obscure the cross is the same in each case.

5. (a) Carboxyl group

   (b) $CH_3OH \longrightarrow CH_3COOH$
   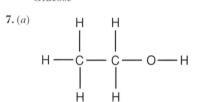
   1 mole   1 mole
   32 g   60 g
   16 g $\longrightarrow$ 30 g

6. (a) They provide the body with energy

   (b) Carbon, hydrogen and oxygen

   (c) Starch
   Sucrose
   Glucose

7. (a)

   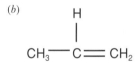

   (b) (i) Ethanol → Ethene + water
   (ii) To prevent suckback
   (iii) It is in a different state from the reactants
   (iv) 1 gram; the same

8. (a) (i) Methylpropane

   (ii) Addition

   (b)

   $$CH_3 - \overset{\overset{\displaystyle H}{|}}{C} = CH_2$$

9. (a) (i) Condensation
   (ii) Amide link
   (iii) So that both ends of each monomer react and a polymer chain can form

   (b) Toughness or strength

10. (a) Glows red or glows brightly

   (b) The aim of the experiment was to place the metals copper, magnesium and zinc in order of reactivity.

   (c) Do not look directly at the burning magnesium

11. (a) Precipitation

   (b) (i) $Pb^{2+}(aq) + 2I^-(aq) \rightarrow Pb^{2+}(I^-)_2(s)$
   (ii) Spectator ions

12. (a) Exothermic

   (b) (i) Hydrogen gas forms an explosive mixture with air
   (ii) Oxidation

   (c) Because iron is lower in reactivity, magnesium will lose electrons more quickly when attached to it
   or
   Iron acts as a catalyst

13. (a) (i)   Number of moles = Volume(1) ×
                                                 Concentration

                   = 0·1 × 1

                   = 0·1

     (ii)   0·3 mol

  (b) (i)   An acid where only some of the molecules dissociate to ions in water.

     (ii)   Description of any method which shows difference eg
Reaction with a metal or metal carbonate
or
conductivity
or
pH

CHEMISTRY INTERMEDIATE 2 2007

SECTION A

1. B	**2.** D	**3.** A
4. D	**5.** C	**6.** A
7. B	**8.** B	**9.** D
10. D	**11.** A	**12.** B
13. C	**14.** B	**15.** D
16. C	**17.** B	**18.** B
19. D	**20.** A	**21.** B
22. C	**23.** C	**24.** D
25. A	**26.** B	**27.** C
28. B	**29.** A	**30.** D

SECTION B

1. (a)

In the nucleus		
Name of particle	Relative mass	Charge
Proton	1	+1
Neutron	1	0

Outside the nucleus		
Name of particle	Relative mass	Charge
Electron	almost zero	-/negative

  (b) (i)   2

     (ii)   X

2. (a) 1·45

  (b) (i)   Reactant and catalyst are in the same state.

     (ii)   amber/would be the same

3. (a) delocalised (free) electrons/electrons are free to move/electrons can pass through

  (b) (i)   Neutralisation

     (ii)   (Polar) Covalent

4. (a) (i)   (aq)

     (ii)   (Burning splint) burns with a pop/squeak

  (b) 1 mole ⟶ 1 mole
    24·3 g ⟶ 2 g
    4·9 g ⟶ 4·9/24·3 x 2
                  =0·4 g

5. (a)

(b) 2-methylpropane-1-thiol/2methylpropane-1-thiol/
2methylpropane 1 thiol

(c) Sulphur dioxide/SO_2

6. (a)

Hydrocarbon	Molecular formula	Observation with bromine solution	Saturated or unsaturated
A	C_6H_{14}	no change	saturated
B	C_6H_{12}	bromine decolorises	unsaturated
C	C_6H_{12}	no change	saturated
D	C_6H_{10}	bromine decolorises	unsaturated

(b) Using safety gloves./ Washing off any spills with sodium thiosulphate.

(c) Hexene or any isomer of hexene with double bond

7. (a) Carbon to carbon double bond/double bond

(b)

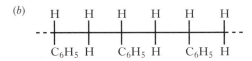

(c) poly(phenylethene)/polyphenylethene

8. (a) $2C_2H_5OH + 2CO_2$

(b) (i)

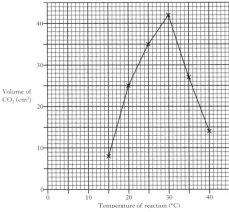

Volume of CO_2 (cm³)

Temperature of reaction (°C)

(ii) Enzyme has been denatured/
destroyed/changes shape./Enzyme can't
function/doesn't work.

9. (a)

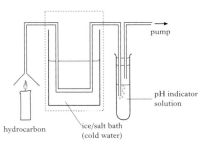

pump

pH indicator solution

hydrocarbon   ice/salt bath (cold water)

(b) Carbon dioxide dissolves to form an acid
solution./In solution carbon dioxide is acidic.

10. (a)

O H
‖ │
—C–N—

(b)

H H O H H O H H O H H O
│ │ ‖ │ │ ‖ │ │ ‖ │ │ ‖
—N–C–C–N–C–C–N–C–C–N–C–C—
│   │   │   │
H   H–C–H   H   H
        │
        H

(c) Condensation

11. (a) Iron loses electrons to the copper./ Electrons 'flow'
from iron to copper./ Iron gives sacrificial protection
to copper.

(b) Seawater contains ions (which act as an electrolyte)./It
is a better electrolyte/contains more ions.

(c) Fe_2O_3 **or** $(Fe^{3+})_2(O^{2-})_3$

12. (a) Electrode A/Positive electrode

(b) $2Na^+ + 2H^+ \rightarrow 2Na + H_2$

(c) higher

higher

13. (a) (i) 2, 0

(ii) Lithium atoms are too/very reactive./Lithium
ions are more stable/less reactive.

(b) The further the metals are from copper, the greater
the voltage/The higher in the ECS the metal is, the
greater the voltage./The more reactive the higher the
voltage.

14. (a)

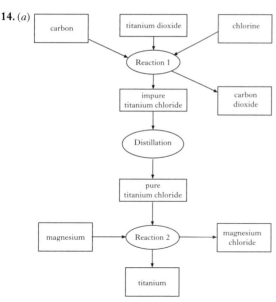

(b) (i)   3·6 g

(ii)   0·075

15. (a) sulphuric acid/H_2SO_4

(b) (i)   To remove any unreacted magnesium/To remove any solid (residue) which is left over/To make sure no solid is left over.

(ii)   Evaporation/boil off water

(c) The energy of the products is less than that of the reactants/Energy decreases from reactants to products, therefore energy is lost/Reactants have higher chemical energy.

CHEMISTRY INTERMEDIATE 2 2008

SECTION A

1. B	2. C	3. C
4. D	5. D	6. A
7. A	8. D	9. A
10. C	11. D	12. C
13. D	14. C	15. B
16. A	17. C	18. D
19. A	20. C	21. B
22. C	23. B	24. A
25. A	26. D	27. D
28. D	29. C	30. D

SECTION B

1. (a) Transition (metal)

(b) (i)

	Number of protons	Number of neutrons
$^{63}_{29}Cu$	29	34
$^{65}_{29}Cu$	29	36

(ii)   isotopes

2. (a) 46g

(b) (i)   46-37 = 9 g

(ii)   Filtration/filter/filtering

3. (a) $4N_2O + CH_4 \rightarrow 4N_2 + CO_2 + 2H_2O$ (or multiples of)

(b) Different (physical) state/form from reactants

(c) Products released/move/leave from catalyst surface

(d) *Either:* Sulphur poisons the catalyst

or Sulphur blocks the active sites

or Sulphur prevents reactants from binding/adsorbing

4. (a) Breakdown of a compound/solution (to its elements) by passing electricity through it.

(b) *Any one from:*

   • Allows the products to be identified
   • To make sure the products are produced at only one electrode
   • Direction of electrons stays the same

   • Electrodes keep the same charge

(c) (i)   *Bubbles of gas-* Positive
      Brown solid formed- Negative

(ii)   By carefully smelling the gas/Smells like a swimming pool/Wafting the gas carefully to your nose
      or (Bleaches) blue litmus paper

5. (a) Tetrahedral/Tetrahedron

(b) (i)

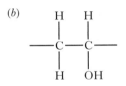

or CF_3CH_2F **or** CHF_2CHF_2

(ii) Chlorine/Cl/Cl_2

(iii) Shorter atmospheric life/biodegrades faster

6. (a) hydroxyl

(b)

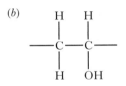

(c) *Any one from:*

- Soluble in water/dissolves
- Breaks down in water
- Degrades in water
- Disintegrates in water

7. (a) *Any one from:*

- Man-made/made by chemists/scientists/man
- Does not occur naturally
- Not natural

(b)

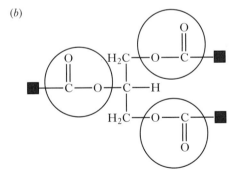

(c) Glycerol/glycerine
or Propan-1,2,3-triol

8. (a) Carbon-carbon double bond

or $C=C$
or Double covalent bond

(b) Absorption at 2800–3000 and at 3600

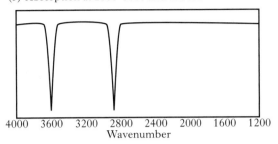

9. (a) Glucose/$C_6H_{12}O_6$

(b) Iodine/I/I_2

(c) (i)

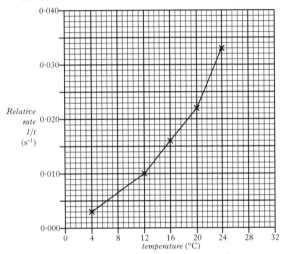

(ii) $1 \div 0.0125 = 80$ secs

10. (a) *Any one from:*

- Protein molecules become unravelled
- The bonds holding the protein molecules are broken
- Shape of the molecule is changed
- Specific shape is changed
- Destroyed

(b) Using an acid/marinating in lime juice/ marinating in citric acid

(c) *Any one from:*

- Bonds are weak
- Bonds are not strong
- Polar bonds are weak
- Hydrogen bonds are weak

10. (*d*)

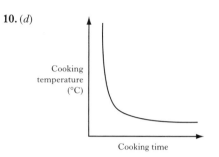

Cooking temperature (°C) vs Cooking time

11. (*a*)

2 moles Al	→	6 moles Ag
54 g	→	648 g
1 g	→	648 ÷ 54 g
0·135 g	→	648 ÷ 54 × 0·135 g
		= 1·62 g

(*b*) Measure mass of beaker at start and again at the end. (Should have decreased.)
Find mass difference

12. (*a*) Carbon dioxide (CO_2)

(*b*) $C_6H_8O_7$

(*c*) weak

13. (*a*) Precipitation

(*b*) Nitric (acid)/hydrogen nitrate/HNO_3

(*c*) Red

14. (*a*) *Any one from:*
- Completes the circuit
- Allows ions to move
- To allow electricity to flow freely
- Carry current

(*b*) (i) Oxidation/loss of electrons

(ii) Aluminium hydroxide/$Al(OH)_3$

15. (*a*) $KMnO_4$

(*b*) Provides reaction with oxygen/Releases oxygen when heated

(*c*) Reaction would be too vigorous/Reaction would be too violent

CHEMISTRY INTERMEDIATE 2 2009

SECTION A

1.	A	11.	A	21.	D
2.	C	12.	B	22.	B
3.	D	13.	C	23.	A
4.	B	14.	D	24.	D
5.	B	15.	C	25.	C
6.	A	16.	A	26.	C
7.	D	17.	D	27.	A
8.	C	18.	A	28.	C
9.	B	19.	D	29.	A
10.	D	20.	A	30.	B

SECTION B

1. (*a*) 11
13

(*b*) (i)

(ii) The attraction/pull/electrostatic force to the positively charged nucleus (and the (negatively charged) electrons)
Attraction/pull/electrostatic force between (positive) protons

2. (*a*) Potassium permanganate
Water
(Conc.) Sulphuric acid

(*b*) (i) As the atomic number increases the melting point increases

(ii) 470°C ± 20

3. (*a*) Exothermic

(*b*) (i) Both labels + units
Both scales
Plotting points
Joining points

(ii) 13 g

(*c*) Reduces heat loss from beaker to the surroundings

4. (*a*) Fe_2O_3 (s) + $\underline{3}CO$(g) ⟶ $\underline{2}Fe$ (*l*) + $\underline{3}$ CO_2 (g)

(*b*) CO_2 (g) + C (s) ⟶ 2 CO (g)

1 mole	⟶	2 moles
12 g	⟶	56 g
1200 kg	⟶	5600 kg

(c) To provide oxygen (for the reaction which takes place in zone 1)
To make CO_2
For complete combustion

5. (a) (As gases have) different boiling points
Different boiling or melting points

(b) liquid

(c) Neutralisation

6. (a) A substance that is burned/combusts to produce energy/heat

(b) (i) Above zero → 35

(ii) The smaller the number of carbons in the molecule, the more efficient/useful/better (the fuel)

7. (a) Aluminium oxide (Al_2O_3)

(b) (i) Butene/C_4H_8

(ii) (Bromine solution would) decolourise/change from brown to colourless

8. (a) Ethyne/etyne

(b) (i)

(ii) Bromines are not attached to adjacent carbon atoms

9. (a)

(b) Amino acids

(c)

10. (a) Starch + water → glucose

(b) Fermentation

Anaerobic respiration

(c)

CH_3COOH

(d) Methyl ethanoate

11. (a) Biological catalyst

(b) (i) One which does not completely/partially ionise/dissociate (into ions)

(ii) Titration
Volumetric titration

12. (a) 167 (s)

(b) (Increasing the number of rhubarb cubes) increases the surface area /concentration/ more particles

(c) (i) $\frac{100}{1000} \times = 0.1$ moles

(ii) 0.1 moles reacts with $5/2 \times 0.1 = 0.25$ moles

13. (a) ...until no more solid reacts/until it no longer reacts

(b) To ensure that all of the acid is reacted

(c) $+ CO_2 (g) + H_2O (l)$

14. (a) Fe_2O_3

(b) $Fe^{2+} (aq) \rightarrow Fe^{3+} (aq) + e^-$

(c) Iron loses electrons to (less reactive) lead

15. (a) $2OH^- (aq) + 2H^+ (aq) \rightarrow 2 H_2O (l)$

(b) (i) Barium hydroxide solution contains a higher concentration of hydroxide ions

(ii) There are no free ions in solution

Hey! I've done it

BrightRED
PUBLISHING

Published by Bright Red Publishing Ltd, 6 Stafford Street, Edinburgh, EH3 7AU
Tel: 0131 220 5804, Fax: 0131 220 6710, enquiries: sales@brightredpublishing.co.uk,
www.brightredpublishing.co.uk

Official SQA answers to 978-1-84948-039-0
2006-2009